Contents

CONTENTS

PAGE

PAGE

TABLES

Use of guidance

THE APPROVED DOCUMENTS

This document is one of a series that has been approved and issued by the Secretary of State for the purpose of providing practical guidance with respect to the requirements of Schedule 1 to and Regulation 7 of the Building Regulations 2010 for England and Wales (SI 2010/2214).

At the back of this document is a list of all the documents that have been approved and issued by the Secretary of State for this purpose.

Approved Documents are intended to provide guidance for some of the more common building situations. However, there may well be alternative ways of achieving compliance with the requirements. **Thus there is no obligation to adopt any particular solution contained in an Approved Document if you prefer to meet the relevant requirement in some other way.**

Other requirements

The guidance contained in an Approved Document relates only to the particular requirements of the Regulations which the document addresses. The building work will also have to comply with the requirements of any other relevant paragraphs in Schedule 1 to the Regulations.

There are Approved Documents which give guidance on each of the Parts of Schedule 1 and on Regulation 7.

LIMITATION ON REQUIREMENTS

In accordance with regulation 8, the requirements in Parts A to D, F to K (except for paragraphs H2 and J7) of Schedule 1 to the Building Regulations do not require anything to be done except for the purpose of securing reasonable standards of health and safety for persons in or about buildings (and any others who may be affected by buildings or matters connected with buildings). This is one of the categories of purpose for which building regulations may be made.

Paragraphs H2 and J7 are excluded from Regulation 8 because they deal directly with prevention of the contamination of water. Parts E and M (which deal, respectively, with resistance to the passage of sound, and access to and use of buildings) are excluded from Regulation 8 because they address the welfare and convenience of building users. Part L is excluded from Regulation 8 because it addresses the conservation of fuel and power. All these matters are amongst the purposes, other than health and safety, that may be addressed by Building Regulations.

MATERIALS AND WORKMANSHIP

Any building work which is subject to the requirements imposed by Schedule 1 to the Building Regulations shall be carried out in accordance with regulation 7. Guidance on meeting these requirements on materials and workmanship is contained in Approved Document 7.

Building Regulations are made for specific purposes, primarily the health and safety, welfare and convenience of people and for energy conservation. Standards and other technical specifications may provide relevant guidance to the extent that they relate to these considerations. However, they may also address other aspects of performance or matters which, although they relate to health and safety etc., are not covered by the Building Regulations.

When an Approved Document makes reference to a named standard, the relevant version of the standard to which it refers is the one listed at the end of the publication. However, if this version has been revised or updated by the issuing standards body, the new version may be used as a source of guidance provided it continues to address the relevant requirements of the Regulations.

---

[1] As implemented by the Construction Products Regulations 1991 (SI 1991/1620).

[2] As implemented by the Construction Products (Amendment) Regulations 1994 (SI 1994/3051).

MIXED USE DEVELOPMENT

In mixed use developments part of a building may be used as a dwelling while another part has a non-domestic use. In such cases, if the requirements of the Regulations for dwellings and non-domestic use differ, the requirements for non-domestic use should apply in any shared parts of the building.

THE WORKPLACE (HEALTH, SAFETY AND WELFARE) REGULATIONS 1992

The Workplace (Health, Safety and Welfare) Regulations 1992 as amended by The Health and Safety (Miscellaneous Amendments) Regulations 2002 (SI 2002/2174) contain some requirements which affect building design. The main requirements are now covered by the Building Regulations, but for further information see: 'Workplace health, safety and welfare. Workplace (Health, Safety and Welfare) Regulations 1992, Approved Code of Practice' L24. Published by HSE Books 1992 (ISBN 0 7176 0413 6).

The Workplace (Health, Safety and Welfare) Regulations 1992 apply to the common parts of flats and similar buildings if people such as cleaners and caretakers are employed to work in these common parts. Where the requirements of the Building Regulations that are covered by this Part do not apply to dwellings, the provisions may still be required in the situations described above in order to satisfy the Workplace Regulations.

THE EQUALITY ACT 2010 AND THE EQUALITY ACT 2010 (DISABILITY) REGULATIONS 2010

The Equality Act 2010 (the EA) brings together existing equalities legislation, including the Disability Discrimination Act 1995, with the aims of strengthening and also harmonising existing provisions into a single streamlined framework of equalities legislation to deliver better outcomes for the protected groups listed.

The EA (http://www.legislation.gov.uk/ukpga/2010/15/contents) imposes a duty to make reasonable adjustments to a physical feature in order to comply with the requirements set out in section 20 of the EA. The duty is set out in Schedule 2 (in relation to public functions and service providers); Schedule 8 (in relation to employers) and Schedule 15 (in relation to associations) of the EA.

Although the guidance in this Approved Document, if followed, tends to demonstrate compliance with Part M of the Building Regulations, this does not necessarily equate to compliance with the obligations and duties set out in the EA. This is because service providers and employers are required by the EA to make reasonable adjustment to any physical feature which might put a disabled person at a substantial disadvantage compared to a non-disabled person. In some instances this will include designing features or making reasonable adjustments to features which are outside the scope of Approved Document M. It remains for the persons undertaking building works to consider if further provision, beyond that described in Approved Document M, is appropriate.

10 Year Exemption for service providers, local authorities and associations

An exemption setting out when an adjustment is not reasonable in relation to design standards is provided in regulation 9 (Reasonableness and design standards) of and the Schedule to the Equality Act 2010 (Disability) Regulations 2010 (the Regulations).

Regulation 9 prescribes circumstances in which it is not reasonable for a provider of services, a public authority carrying out its functions, or an association to remove or alter a physical feature which has been provided to assist access to the building or its facilities and which accords with the relevant design standard. The Schedule to the Regulations provides that a physical feature satisfies the relevant design standard if it complied with the objectives, design considerations and provisions set out in the edition of Approved Document M that applied at the time the building works were carried out.

This provision will not apply where more than 10 years have elapsed since:

- the day on which construction or installation of the feature was completed; or

- in the case of a physical feature provided as part of a larger building project, the day on which the works in relation to that project were completed.

Applicants should be aware that this is not a blanket exemption from duties under the EA, and relates only to the duty to make reasonable adjustments to physical features built in strict accordance with the guidance provided in the relevant approved document. As with all other types of building work, service providers will still need to consider the needs of disabled people which are outside the scope of Approved Document M. It is for applicants, not building control bodies, to consider how these obligations are to be met.

Relationship with guidance in Approved Document K (Protection from falling collision and impact)

Where applicable, parts of this Approved Document state that the requirements of Part M will be satisfied by compliance with the applicable parts of the guidance within Approved Document K (Protection from falling, collision and impact). Compliance with these applicable requirements set out in Approved Document K in these circumstances will be regarded as compliance with a relevant design standard for the purposes of regulation 9 and the Schedule to the Regulations.

The Requirements

This Approved Document, which takes effect on 1 May 2004, deals with the requirements of Part M of Schedule 1 to the Building Regulations 2010.

Requirement	*Limits on application*
PART M ACCESS TO AND USE OF BUILDINGS	
Access and use	The requirements of this Part do not apply to:
M1. Reasonable provision shall be made for people to:	
(a) gain access to; and	(a) an extension of or material alteration of a dwelling; or
(b) use	
the building and its facilities.	(b) any part of a building which is used solely to enable the building or any service or fitting in the building to be inspected, repaired or maintained.
Access to extensions to buildings other than dwellings	
M2. Suitable independent access shall be provided to the extension where reasonably practicable.	Requirement M2 does not apply where suitable access to the extension is provided through the building that is extended.
Sanitary conveniences in extensions to buildings other than dwellings	
M3. If sanitary conveniences are provided in any building that is to be extended, reasonable provision shall be made within the extension for sanitary conveniences.	Requirement M3 does not apply where there is reasonable provision for sanitary conveniences elsewhere in the building, such that people occupied in, or otherwise having occasion to enter the extension, can gain access to and use those sanitary conveniences.
Sanitary conveniences in dwellings	
M4. (1) Reasonable provision shall be made in the entrance storey for sanitary conveniences, or where the entrance storey contains no habitable rooms, reasonable provision for sanitary conveniences shall be made in either the entrance storey or the principal storey.	
(2) In this paragraph 'entrance storey' means the storey which contains the principal entrance and 'principal storey' means the storey nearest to the entrance storey which contains a habitable room, or if there are two such storeys equally near, either such storey.	

Notes

Means of escape in case of fire: the scope of Part M and AD M is limited to matters of access to, into and use of a building. It does not extend to means of escape in the event of fire, for which reference should be made to Approved Document B – 'Fire Safety'.

Stairs and ramps: Approved Document K (Protection from falling, collision and impact) contains guidance on internal and external steps, stairs and ramps when they are part of the building. Additional guidance is provided in this Approved Document when external stepped and ramped access also form part of the principal entrances and alternative accessible entrances, and when they form part of the access route to the building from the boundary of the site and car parking.

Manifestation on glazed doors and glazed screens: Approved Document K (Protection from falling, collision and impact) contains guidance on manifestation.

BS 8300:2001 Design of buildings and their approaches to meet the needs of disabled people. Code of Practice: this supersedes BS 5619:1978 and BS 5810:1979. BS 8300 provides guidance on good practice in the design of domestic and non-domestic buildings and their approaches so that they are convenient to use by disabled people. The design recommendations are based on user trials and validated desk studies which formed part of a research project commissioned in 1997 and 2001 by DETR. The guidance in this Approved Document is based on and is complementary to the BS, although the BS contains much additional material that is not apt for, or not considered appropriate for, inclusion in guidance accompanying regulation. Also, in a few cases, the guidance in AD M differs from the recommendation in BS 8300. Compliance with the recommendations in the BS, therefore, while ensuring good practice, is not necessarily equivalent to compliance with the guidance in AD M.

Attention is drawn to the following extracts from The Building Regulations 2010.

Interpretation (Regulation 2)

Regulation 2 contains the following definition:

'independent access' means in relation to a part of a building (including any extension to that building) a route of access to that part which does not require the user to pass through any other part of the building.

The meanings of the expressions 'institution', 'public building' and 'shop' used in Regulation 5 are explained in Regulation 2.

Meaning of material change of use (regulation 5)

For the purposes of paragraph 8 (1)(e) of Schedule 1 to the Act and for the purposes of these Regulations, there is a material change of use where there is a change in the purposes for which or the circumstances in which a building is used, so that after the change:

a. the building is used as a dwelling, where previously it was not;

b. the building contains a flat, where previously it did not;

c. the building is used as an hotel or a boarding house, where previously it was not;

d. the building is used as an institution, where previously it was not;

e. the building is used as a public building, where previously it was not;

f. the building is not a building described in Classes 1 to 6 in Schedule 2, where previously it was;

g. the building, which contains at least one dwelling, contains a greater or lesser number of dwellings than it did previously;

h. the building contains a room for residential purposes, where previously it did not;

I. the building, which contains at least one room for residential purposes, contains a greater or lesser number of such rooms than it did previously; or

j. the building is used as a shop, where previously it was not.

Requirements relating to material change of use (Regulation 6)

1. Where there is a material change of use of the whole of a building, such work, if any, shall be carried out as is necessary to ensure that the building complies with the applicable requirements of the following paragraphs of Schedule 1:

a. in all cases,

  B1 (means of warning and escape)

  B2 (internal fire spread – linings)

  B3 (internal fire spread – structure)

  B4(2) (external fire spread – roofs)

  B5 (access and facilities for the fire service)

  C2(c) (interstitial and surface condensation)

  F1 (means of ventilation)

  G3(1) to (3) (hot water supply and systems)

  G4 (sanitary conveniences and washing facilities)

  G5 (bathrooms)

  G6 (kitchen and food preparation areas)

  H1 (foul water drainage)

  H6 (solid waste storage)

  J1 to J4 (combustion appliances)

  L1 (conservation of fuel and power – dwellings)

  P1 (electrical safety);

b. in the case of a material change of use described in Regulations 5(c), (d), (e) or (f), A1 to A3 (structure);

c. in the case of a building exceeding 15m in height, B4(1) (external fire spread – walls);

d. in the case of material change of use described in regulation 5(a), (b), (c), (d), (g), (h), (i) or, where the material change provides new residential accommodation, (f), C1(2) (resistance to contaminants);

e. in the case of material change of use described in Regulation 5(a), C4 (resistance to weather and ground moisture);

f. in the case of a material change of use described in Regulation 5(a), (b), (c), (g), (h) or (i), E1 to E3 (resistance to the passage of sound);

g. in the case of a material change of use described in Regulation 5(e), where the public building consists of or contains a school, E4 (acoustic conditions in schools);

h. in the case of a material change of use described in Regulation 5(c), (d), (e) or (j), M1 (access and use).

2. Where there is a material change of use of part only of a building, such work, if any, shall be carried out as is necessary to ensure that:

a. that part complies in all cases with any applicable requirements referred to in paragraph (1)(a);

b. in a case to which sub-paragraphs (b), (d), (e) or (f) of paragraph (1) apply, that part complies with the requirements referred to in the relevant sub-paragraph;

c. in a case to which sub-paragraph (c) of paragraph (1) applies, the whole building complies with the requirement referred to in that sub-paragraph; and

d. in a case to which sub-paragraph (i) of paragraph (1) applies:

  i. that part and any sanitary conveniences provided in or in connection with that part comply with the requirements referred to in that sub-paragraph; and

  ii. the building complies with requirement M1(a) of Schedule 1 to the extent that reasonable provision is made to provide either suitable independent access to that part or suitable access through the building to that part.

Section 0: General guidance

PERFORMANCE

In the Secretary of State's view the requirements of Part M will be met by making reasonable provision to ensure that buildings are accessible and usable.

People, regardless of disability, age or gender, should be able to:

a. gain access to buildings and to gain access within buildings and use their facilities, both as visitors and as people who live or work in them;

b. use sanitary conveniences in the principal storey of a new dwelling.

The provisions are expected to enable occupants with disabilities to cope better with reducing mobility and to 'stay put' longer in their own homes. The provisions are not necessarily expected to facilitate fully independent living for all people with disabilities.

Where the requirements apply

Application of Part M

0.1   The requirements apply if:

a. a non-domestic building or a dwelling is newly erected;

b. an existing non-domestic building is extended, or undergoes a material alteration; or

c. an existing building or part of an existing building undergoes a material change of use to a hotel or boarding house, institution, public building or shop.

The terms 'institution', 'public building' and 'shop' are explained in regulation 2.

It should be noted that, regardless of compliance with Building Regulations, there will be obligations under the Equality Act 2010 for service providers and employers to consider barriers created by physical features in buildings.

Extensions and material alterations: dwellings

0.2   Under Regulation 4(3), where any building is extended, or undergoes a material alteration, the building work must be carried out so that after it has been completed the building complies with the applicable requirements of Schedule 1, or, where it did not fully comply with any applicable requirement, it is no more unsatisfactory than before.

0.3   This rule applies to domestic as well as to non-domestic buildings. Under the Limits on Application in Part M, Part M does not apply to an extension of, or a material alteration of, a dwelling. However, an extension of a dwelling, or a material alteration of a dwelling, must not make the building less satisfactory in relation to Part M than it was before.

0.4   Under regulation 3, the expression 'material alteration' is defined by reference to a list of 'relevant requirements' in Schedule 1. That list includes Part M. This means that an alteration of a dwelling is a material alteration if the work would result in the dwelling not complying with Part M where previously it did. Alternatively, if the dwelling did not previously comply with Part M, the dwelling should not be more unsatisfactory in relation to Part M after the material alteration. It is irrelevant whether or not the dwelling was subject to Part M at the time of its construction. Under the general Limits on Application of Part M, the requirements of that Part do not apply to an extension of or a material alteration of a dwelling. This means that the extension or alteration work itself need not comply with Part M. However, a planned alteration to a dwelling that has the potential to reduce the compliance of the dwelling as a whole with Part M must be carried out in such a way that there is no reduction in the extent of Part M compliance. Similarly, an extension of a dwelling need not itself comply with Part M, but it must not result in the dwelling being less compliant with Part M. The following examples illustrate these points.

Example 1: a planned project involving removal of a WC in the entrance storey of a dwelling would be a material alteration if it is the only WC in that storey and the storey contains habitable rooms. The WC must *not* be removed or made less compliant with Part M, unless another WC is provided in the entrance storey that is no less satisfactory in terms of compliance with Part M than the old one.

Example 2: a planned extension (not exempt under Class VII of Schedule 2) enclosing the principal entrance of a dwelling must not make the dwelling less satisfactory in terms of requirement M1 than it was before. It must be no less easy for people, including disabled people, to gain access to the dwelling, either via the extension and the original entrance point, or (subject to the guidance in Section 6 of this AD) via a suitable alternative entrance.

Extensions of non-domestic buildings

0.5 An extension to a non-domestic building should be treated in the same manner as a new building, as regards its own compliance with Part M. Under the new Requirement M2 there must be suitable independent access to the extension where reasonably practicable. Under the Limits on Application, Requirement M2 does not apply where the building that is extended complies with Requirement M1(a) so as to provide suitable access through the building to the extension. The concept of access encompasses access from the boundary of the site and from on-site car parking where provided.

0.6 If the owners of a building prefer not to provide independent access to a planned extension, it is open to them either to demonstrate that the existing building and the approach to it already comply with Requirement M1(a), so that the Limit on Application of Requirement M2 applies, or to modify the existing building and/or the approach to it so that the Limit on Application applies. Such modification work would be a material alteration. The extensions and the alterations of the existing building could be planned and carried out as a single project.

0.7 In judging whether access provision relying on the existing building is sufficient for the Limit on Application of Requirement M2 to apply, and in judging whether it is reasonably practicable for suitable independent access to be provided, practical constraints and cost considerations will be relevant – see also 'Access Strategies' paragraphs 0.20 and 0.25 below.

0.8 Under new Requirement M3, if sanitary conveniences are provided in any building that is to be extended, reasonable provision must be made within the extension for sanitary conveniences. However, under the Limit on Application of Requirement M3, this requirement does not apply if there is reasonable provision for people using the extension to gain access to and to use sanitary conveniences in the existing building. As in the case of access to an extension, it is open to building owners preferring not to make provisions for sanitary conveniences in a planned extension either to demonstrate that reasonable provision already exists in, or to modify, the existing building so that the Limit on Application of Requirement M3 applies. In this case, too, the extension and the modifications to the existing building could be planned and carried out as a single project.

Material alterations of non-domestic buildings

0.9 Under regulation 4, where an alteration of a non-domestic building is a material alteration, the work itself must comply, where relevant, with Requirement M1. This means that alterations to features relevant to the compliance of a building with Part M, such as entrances or arrangements for people to get from one level to another within the building, must result in features that comply with Requirement M1. Where new features relevant to the compliance of a building with Part M are provided, these must also comply with Requirement M1. Reasonable provision must be made for people to gain access to and to use new or altered sanitary conveniences. The building as a whole, including access to it from the site boundary and from on-site car parking where provided, must be no less compliant with Requirement M1 following a material alteration of a building. In the context of a material alteration of a building, it is not necessary, as regards the Building Regulations, to upgrade access to the building entrance from the site boundary and from on-site car parking where provided. However, attention is drawn to the note in paragraph 1, above about the Equality Act.

Material changes of use

0.10 Under regulation 6, as amended, where there is a material change of use of the whole of a building to a hotel or boarding house, an institution, a public building or a shop, the building must be upgraded, if necessary, so as to comply with M1 (Access and use). The terms 'institution', 'public building' and 'shop' are explained in regulation 2. In particular, it should be noted that 'shop' includes use as a restaurant, bar or public house.

0.11 Under regulation 6, as amended, if an existing building undergoes a change of use such that *part* is used as a hotel or boarding house, an institution, a public building or a shop, such work if any shall be carried out as is necessary to ensure that:

- there is reasonable provision for people to gain access to that part from the site boundary and from on-site car parking where provided, either by means of an independent access or by means of a route to and through the building;

- that part itself complies with M1 (access and use); and

- any sanitary conveniences provided in, or in connection with, that part comply with Requirement M1: if users of that part have the use of sanitary conveniences elsewhere in the building, there must be reasonable provision for people to gain access to and use that sanitary accommodation, upgraded if need be.

Developers will need to agree how they have assessed what is reasonable provision with the relevant building control body as set out in paragraphs 0.20 to 0.25.

0.12 Where a material change of use results in a building being used in part as a hotel or boarding house, institution, public building or shop, and in part as a dwelling, regard should be had to the guidance in Sections 1 to 5 of this Approved Document in relation to the relevant non-domestic accommodation and to the common parts (see also MIXED USE DEVELOPMENT under Use of Guidance).

Car parking and setting down

0.13 Part M applies to those features, outside the building, which are needed to provide access to the building from the edge of the site and from car parking and setting down points within the site.

What requirements apply

0.14 If Part M applies, reasonable provision should be made in:

i. Buildings other than dwellings

a. so that people, regardless of disability, age or gender, can reach the principal entrance to the building and other entrances described in this Approved Document from the site boundary, from car parking within the site, and from other buildings on the same site (such as a university campus, a school or a hospital);

b. so that elements of the building do not constitute a hazard to users, especially people with impaired sight, but rather assist in wayfinding;

c. so that people, regardless of disability, age or gender, can have access into, and within, any storey of the building and to the building's facilities, subject to the usual gender-related conventions regarding sanitary accommodation;

d. for suitable accommodation for people in wheelchairs, or people with other disabilities, in audience or spectator seating;

e. for aids to communication for people with an impairment of hearing or sight in auditoria, meeting rooms, reception areas, ticket offices and at information points; and

f. for sanitary accommodation for the users of the building.

ii. Dwellings

a. so that people, including disabled people, can reach the principal, or suitable alternative, entrance to the dwelling from the point of access;

b. so that people, including disabled people, can gain access into and within the principal storey of the dwelling; and

c. for WC provision at no higher storey than the principal storey.

'Principal storey' is defined in Requirement M4.

Educational establishments

0.15 From 1 April 2001, maintained schools ceased to have exemption from the Building Regulations. Certain school-specific standards relating to Parts K and M contained in the DfES 1997 Constructional Standards as described in Circular DfES/0142/2001 are subsumed in this revision to AD M (see 1.33 – Note re: (l) and (m), 1.36, 1.37 (b).

0.16 Purpose-built student living accommodation, including that in the form of flats as defined in regulation 2(1), should be treated as hotel/motel accommodation in respect of space requirements and internal facilities (see 4.17 to 4.24).

Historic buildings

0.17 Historic buildings include:

a. listed buildings,

b. buildings situated in conservation areas,

c. buildings which are of architectural and historical interest and which are referred to as a material consideration in a local authority's development plan,

d. buildings of architectural and historic interest within national parks, areas of outstanding natural beauty and world heritage sites,

e. vernacular buildings of traditional form and construction.

0.18 The need to conserve the special characteristics of such historic buildings must be recognised. They are a finite resource with cultural importance. In such work the aim should be to improve accessibility where and to the extent that it is practically possible, always provided that the work does not prejudice the character of the historic building, or increase the risk of long-term deterioration to the building fabric or fittings. In arriving at an appropriate balance between historic building conservation and accessibility, it would be appropriate to take into account the advice of the local authority's conservation and access officers, and English Heritage or CADW: Welsh Historic Monuments, as well as the views of local access groups, in order to make the building as accessible as possible.

0.19 Particular issues relating to work in historic buildings that warrant sympathetic treatment and where advice from others could therefore be beneficial include:

a. restoring the historic character of a building that had been subject to previous inappropriate alteration, e.g. replacement windows, doors and rooflights;

b. rebuilding a former historic building (e.g. following a fire or filling in a gap site in a terrace);

c. the choice of appropriate construction materials and techniques, e.g. making provisions enabling the fabric to 'breathe' to control moisture and potential long-term decay problems: see Information Sheet No. 4 from The Society for the Protection of Ancient Buildings (SPAB).

Access strategy

0.20 It is important that applicants clearly communicate to the building control body how their chosen approach to meeting the accessibility needs of the likely end-users of a building and its facilities demonstrates compliance with the requirements of Part M of the Building Regulations. The guidance in this Approved Document is designed to indicate only one way in which those requirements may be met. Whilst alternative, equally satisfactory ways of meeting the requirements can be adopted depending on the size, scale, nature and intended use of the building they must still demonstrate compliance with the relevant functional requirement.

0.21 Where alternative solutions are proposed, the onus remains with the applicant to demonstrate that those solutions are appropriate and meet the requirements, for example by showing that it is equivalent to the provisions set out in this Approved Document. This should include the use of appropriate research evidence or reference to recognised British Standards as necessary to support the chosen approach. It is advisable to ensure that the appropriate level of provision is agreed with the building control body prior to commencing building work, as retrospective alterations can be costly and disruptive.

0.22 Applicants should therefore seek to engage with building control bodies at the earliest possible stage to identify key issues and risks, and to discuss the best way to demonstrate the access strategy for the building work taking place. To ensure satisfactory outcomes, communication between applicants and building control bodies should focus on areas where proposals diverge from the guidance in this Approved Document rather than providing an exhaustive explanation where features are in accordance with the guidance.

0.23 Provision of a written Access strategy is not required to accompany a building control application though it may be useful in some circumstances. The key focus should be on ensuring that applicants and building control bodies are agreed as to the appropriate level of provision in the completed building work.

0.24 In smaller or simpler works this could be achieved by having a conversation to review the proposals and recording the outcome of discussions by correspondence. In large, complex works or where there are significant constraints

imposed by an existing site, this might involve a written document setting out key aspects of the access approach, supported by annotated drawings as well as face to face meetings to resolve key issues. It is for the building control body and applicant to agree which, if any of these proposed approaches should be used on a case by case basis to ensure that the functional requirements of Part M of the Building Regulations are satisfied. Whichever approach is adopted, the agreed level of provision should be clearly recorded.

0.25 It should be noted that approval of proposed works by a building control body does not by necessity indicate compliance with duties under the Equalities Act 2010. Applicants need to consider these wider equality obligations when undertaking building work and whether provision in some circumstances should exceed that set out within this Approved Document. The relationship between Part M of the Building Regulations and the Equality Act 2010 is set out on page 7 of this Approved Document.

Definitions

0.26 The following meanings apply to terms throughout this Approved Document.

Access, approach, entry or exit.

Accessible, with respect to buildings or parts of buildings, means that people, regardless of disability, age or gender, are able to gain access.

Contrast visually, when used to indicate the visual perception of one element of the building, or fitting within the building, against another means that the difference in light reflectance value between the two surfaces is greater than 30 points. Where illuminance on surfaces is greater than 200 lux, a difference in light reflectance value should be a minimum of 20 points. Where door opening furniture projects beyond the face of the door or otherwise creates enhanced differentiation and shade, a minimum a difference in light reflectance value of 15 points is considered adequate.

For further information, reference should be made to Colour, contrast and perception – Design guidance for internal built environments – Reading University).

Dwelling, means a house or a flat ('flat' is defined in regulation 2(1)). However, new blocks of flats built as student accommodation are to be treated as though they are hotel/motel accommodation in respect of space requirements and internal facilities (see 4.17 to 4.24).

General access stair, a stair intended for all users of a building on a day-to day-basis, as a normal route between levels.

illuminance, the amount of light falling on a surface, measured in lumens per square metre (lm/m^2) or lux (lx).

Level, with respect to the surfaces of a level approach, access routes and landings associated with steps, stairs and ramps means predominantly level, but with a maximum gradient along the direction of travel of 1:60.

Light reflectance value (LRV), the total quantity of visible light reflected by a surface at all wavelengths and directions when illuminated by a light source.

Principal entrance, the entrance which a visitor not familiar with the building would normally expect to approach.

Suitable, with respect to means of access and facilities, means that they are designed for use by people regardless of disability, age or gender, but subject to the usual gender-related conventions regarding sanitary accommodation.

Usable, with respect to buildings or parts of buildings, means that they are convenient for independent use.

Utility stair, a stair used for escape, access for maintenance, or purposes other than as a usual route for moving between levels on a day-to-day basis.

0.30 The following meanings apply only to terms used in the sections on dwellings in this Approved Document.

Common, serving more than one dwelling.

Habitable room, for the purpose of defining the principal storey, means a room used, or intended to be used, for dwelling purposes, including a kitchen but not a bathroom or a utility room.

Maisonette, a self-contained dwelling, but not a dwelling-house, which occupies more than one storey in a building.

Point of access, the point at which a person visiting a dwelling would normally alight from a vehicle which may be within or outside the plot, prior to approaching the dwelling.

Principal entrance, the entrance which a visitor not familiar with the dwelling would normally expect to approach or the common entrance to a block of flats.

Plot gradient, the gradient measured between the finished floor level of the dwelling and the point of access.

Steeply sloping plot, a plot gradient of more than 1:15.

Section 1: Access to buildings other than dwellings

OBJECTIVES

1.1 The aim is to provide a suitable means of access for people from the entrance point at the boundary of the site, and from any car parking that is provided on the site, to the building. It is also important that routes between buildings within a complex are also accessible.

1.2 In designing an approach to the building, it should be recognised that changes in level are difficult for many people to negotiate, including wheelchair users, people who need to use walking aids and people with impaired sight. Access routes that are too narrow can also make it difficult for people to pass each other.

1.3 It is important to be aware that people's capabilities vary. For example, for some people, a stair is easier to use than a ramp.

1.4 The building should be designed, within the overall constraints of space, so that the difference in level between the entrance storey and the site entry point is minimised.

1.5 It is also important that potential hazards on access routes adjacent to buildings, e.g. open windows, are avoided so that people, particularly children and those with impaired sight or hearing, are not injured.

Note: The publication 'Inclusive Mobility: A Guide to Best Practice on Access to Pedestrian and Transport Infrastructure' gives detailed guidance on designing the external environment.

Level approach from the boundary of the site and car parking

Design considerations

1.6 As far as possible, access should be level from the boundary of the site, and from any car parking designated for disabled people, to the principal entrance and any entrance used exclusively for staff or, if either of these is not accessible, to any alternative accessible entrances. If access is generally required between entrances, or between alternative accessible entrances outside the building, this access should as far as possible be level. The site level of accessible entrances should be determined accordingly.

1.7 Where a difference in level between the boundary of the site or car parking designated for disabled people and the building is unavoidable due to site constraints, the approach may have a gentle gradient over a long distance (for all or part/s of the approach) or it may incorporate a number of shorter parts at a steeper gradient, with level landings at intervals as rest points. Generally, gradients within the approach should be as gentle as possible.

1.8 Where the gradient of the approach, whether over its whole length or in part, is 1:20 or steeper, that part of the approach should be designed as ramped access.

1.9 All access routes to principal, or alternative accessible, entrances should be surfaced so that people are able to travel along them easily, without excessive effort and without the risk of tripping or falling.

1.10 There should be sufficient space for people to approach the building, pass others who are travelling in the opposite direction and carry out all necessary manoeuvres.

1.11 A surface width of 1800mm can accommodate any amount of non-vehicular traffic without the need for passing places. A surface width of 1200mm may be acceptable on restricted sites, subject to agreement with the building control body.

1.12 It is important to reduce the risks to people, particularly people with impaired sight, when approaching and passing around the perimeter of the building under all lighting conditions.

Provisions

1.13 A 'level approach' (from the boundary of the site and from car parking spaces designated for disabled people to the principal entrance, to a staff entrance or to an alternative accessible entrance) will satisfy Requirement M1 or M2 if:

a. it has a surface width of at least 1.5m, with passing places, free of obstructions to a height of 2.1m;

b. passing places at least 1.8m wide and at least 2m long are provided within sight of each other (the width of the passing place may be included in the width of the level approach), but in any case spaced at a distance no greater than 50m;

c. the gradient along its length is either no steeper than 1:60 along its whole length, or less steep than 1:20 with level landings (see 1.26(k)) introduced for each 500mm rise of the access (where necessary, between landings), in all cases with a cross-fall gradient no steeper than 1:40;

d. its surface is firm, durable and slip resistant, with undulations not exceeding 3mm under a 1m straight edge for formless materials. Inappropriate materials might be loose sand or gravel;

e. where there are different materials along the access route, they have similar frictional characteristics;

f. the difference in level at joints between paving units is no greater than 5mm, with joints filled flush or, if recessed, no deeper than 5mm and no wider than 10mm or, if unfilled, no wider than 5mm;

g. the route to the principal entrance (or alternative accessible entrance) is clearly identified and well lit;

h. the danger of inadvertently walking into a vehicular access route is minimised by providing a separate pedestrian route and, where there is an uncontrolled crossing point across the vehicular route, this is identified by a buff coloured blister surface (see Diagram 1, and 'Guidance on the use of Tactile Paving Surfaces').

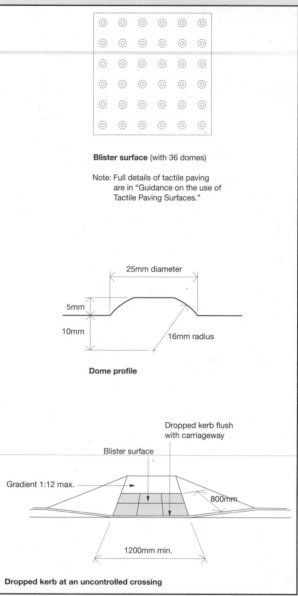

Diagram 1 **Tactile paving and an example of its use at an uncontrolled crossing**

Blister surface (with 36 domes)

Note: Full details of tactile paving are in "Guidance on the use of Tactile Paving Surfaces."

25mm diameter

5mm

10mm

16mm radius

Dome profile

Dropped kerb flush with carriageway

Blister surface

Gradient 1:12 max.

800mm

1200mm min.

Dropped kerb at an uncontrolled crossing

On-site car parking and setting down

Design considerations

1.14 People who need to travel to buildings by car need to be able to park, have sufficient space to enter and leave their vehicle, on occasions move to the rear of their vehicle, then walk, travel in a wheelchair or with pushchairs or luggage, etc. to the principal entrance, the staff entrance or any alternative accessible entrance of the building.

1.15 The surface of a parking bay designated for disabled people, in particular the area surrounding the bay, should allow the safe transfer of a passenger or driver to a wheelchair and transfer from the parking bay to the access route to the building without undue effort, barriers to wheelchairs or hazards from tripping.

1.16 If people need to obtain tickets for pay and display parking, the ticket dispensing machines should be located in a way that allows a person in a wheelchair, or a person of short stature, to gain access close to the machine and reach the payment and ticket dispensing functions.

1.17 People with mobility impairments who arrive as passengers should be able to alight from a vehicle close to the principal entrance, or alternative accessible entrance, of the building in a way that is convenient for entry into the building.

Note: Guidance is available in BS 8300 on:

- the provision of parking bays designated for disabled people in different building types;

- ticket dispensing machines;

- vehicular control barriers; and

- multi-storey car parks.

Provisions

1.18 Car parking and setting down will satisfy Requirement M1 or M2 if:

a. at least one parking bay designated for disabled people is provided on firm and level ground as close as feasible to the principal entrance of the building;

b. the dimensions of the designated parking bays are as shown in Diagram 2 (with a 1200mm accessibility zone between, and a 1200mm safety zone on the vehicular side of, the parking bays, and with a dropped kerb when there is a pedestrian route at the other side of the parking bay);

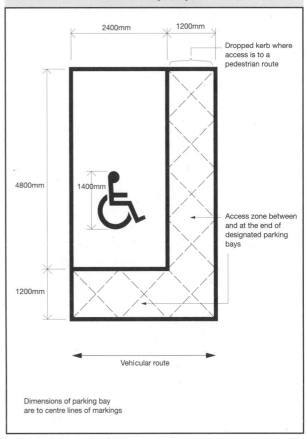

Diagram 2 Parking bay designated for disabled people

2400mm

1200mm

Dropped kerb where access is to a pedestrian route

4800mm

1400mm

Access zone between and at the end of designated parking bays

1200mm

Vehicular route

Dimensions of parking bay are to centre lines of markings

c. the surface of the accessibility zone is firm, durable and slip resistant, with undulations not exceeding 3mm under a 1m straight edge for formless materials. Inappropriate materials might be loose sand or gravel;

d. ticket machines, where necessary for wheelchair users and people of short stature, are adjacent to the designated parking bays for disabled people and have controls between 750mm and 1200mm above the ground and a plinth which does not project in front of the face of the machine in a way that prevents its convenient use;

e. a clearly sign-posted setting down point is located on firm and level ground as close as practicable to the principal or alternative accessible entrance with its surface level with the carriageway at that point to allow convenient access to and from the entrance for people with walking difficulties or people using a wheelchair.

Ramped access

Note: Where there appears to be a conflict between the guidance in Part M and Part K, Part M takes precedence; see the Notes to the Requirements.

Design considerations

1.19 If site constraints necessitate an approach of 1:20 or steeper, an approach incorporating ramped access should be provided. Ramps are beneficial for wheelchair users and people pushing prams, pushchairs and bicycles.

1.20 Gradients should be as shallow as practicable, as steep gradients create difficulties for some wheelchair users who lack the strength to propel themselves up a slope or have difficulty in slowing down or stopping when descending.

1.21 Ramps are also not necessarily safe and convenient for ambulant disabled people. For example, some people who can walk but have restricted mobility find it more difficult to negotiate a ramp than a stair. In addition, adverse weather conditions increase the risk of slipping on a ramp. It is therefore beneficial to have steps as well as a ramp.

1.22 Some people need to be able to stop frequently; for instance to regain strength or breath, or to ease pain.

1.23 Wheelchair users need adequate space to stop on landings, to open and pass through doors without having to reverse into circulation routes or to face the risk of rolling back down slopes.

1.24 Some people have a weakness on one side. This leads to a requirement for support at both sides of ramps.

1.25 If the total rise of a ramped approach is too high, it can be unacceptably tiringfor wheelchair users and some people with walking difficulties, even if a number of rest landings are provided.

Note: Guidance is given in BS 8300 on:

– lighting ramped access.

Provisions

1.26 A ramped access will satisfy Requirement M1 or M2 if:

a. either it is readily apparent or the approach to it is clearly sign-posted;

b. the gradient of a ramp flight and its going between landings are in accordance with Table 1 and Diagram 3;

c. no flight has a going greater than 10m, or a rise of more than 500mm;

Table 1 **Limits for ramp gradients**

Going of a flight	Maximum gradient	Maximum rise
10m	1:20	500mm
5m	1:15	333mm
2m	1:12	166mm

Note:

For goings between 2m and 10m, it is acceptable to interpolate between the maximum gradients, i.e. 1:14 for a 4m going or 1:19 for a 9m going (see Diagram 3).

Diagram 3 **Relationship of ramp gradient to the going of a flight**

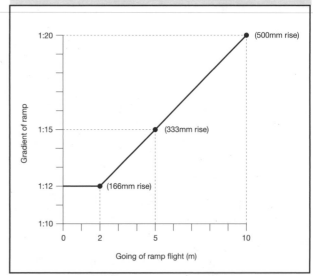

d. there is an alternative means of access for wheelchair users, e.g. a lift, when the total rise is greater than 2m;

e. it has a surface width between walls, upstands or kerbs of at least 1.5m;

f. the ramp surface is slip resistant, especially when wet, and of a colour that contrasts visually with that of the landings;

g. the frictional characteristics of the ramp and landing surfaces are similar;

h. there is a landing at the foot and head of the ramp at least 1.2m long and clear of any door swings or other obstructions;

i. any intermediate landings are at least 1.5m long and clear of any door swings or other obstructions;

j. intermediate landings at least 1800mm wide and 1800mm long are provided as passing places when it is not possible for a wheelchair user to see from one end of the ramp to the other or the ramp has three flights or more;

k. all landings are level, subject to a maximum gradient of 1:60 along their length and a maximum cross-fall gradient of 1:40;

l. there is a handrail on both sides;

m. there is a kerb on the open side of any ramp or landing at least 100mm high, which contrasts visually with the ramp or landing in addition to any guarding required under Part K;

n. clearly sign-posted steps are provided, in addition, when the rise of the ramp is greater than 300mm (equivalent to 2 x 150mm steps).

Stepped access

Note: Where there appears to be a conflict between the guidance in Part M and Part K, Part M takes precedence; see the Notes to the Requirements.

Design considerations

1.27 People with impaired sight risk tripping or losing their balance if there is no warning that steps provide a change in level. The risk is most hazardous at the head of a flight of steps when a person is descending.

1.28 The warning should be placed sufficiently in advance of the hazard to allow time to stop and not be so narrow that it might be missed in a single stride.

1.29 Materials for treads should not present a slip hazard, especially when the surface is wet.

1.30 People should be able to appreciate easily where to place their feet by highlighting nosings and avoiding open rises.

1.31 People who wear callipers or who have stiffness in hip or knee joints are particularly at risk of tripping or catching their feet beneath nosings. People with a weakness on one side or with a sight impairment need the dimensions of the tread to be sufficient for them to be able to place their feet square onto it. If the going is towards the upper end of the dimensional range, the flight may rise to a greater height without the need for an intermediate landing, as the tread is sufficiently deep to allow a person to stand and rest at any point within the flight. It should be noted that excessive rounding of nosings reduces the effective going.

1.32 Many ambulant disabled people find it easier to negotiate a flight of steps than a ramp and, for these people, the presence of handrails for support is essential.

Note: Guidance is given in BS 8300 on:

– lighting stepped access; and

– slip resistance (Annex C).

Provisions

1.33 A stepped access will satisfy Requirement M1 or M2 if:

a. a level landing is provided at the top and bottom of each flight;

b. the unobstructed length of each landing is not less than 1200mm;

c. a 'corduroy' hazard warning surface is provided at top and bottom landings of a series of flights to give advance warning of a change in level in accordance with Diagram 4;

Diagram 4 Stepped access – key dimensions and use of hazard warning surface

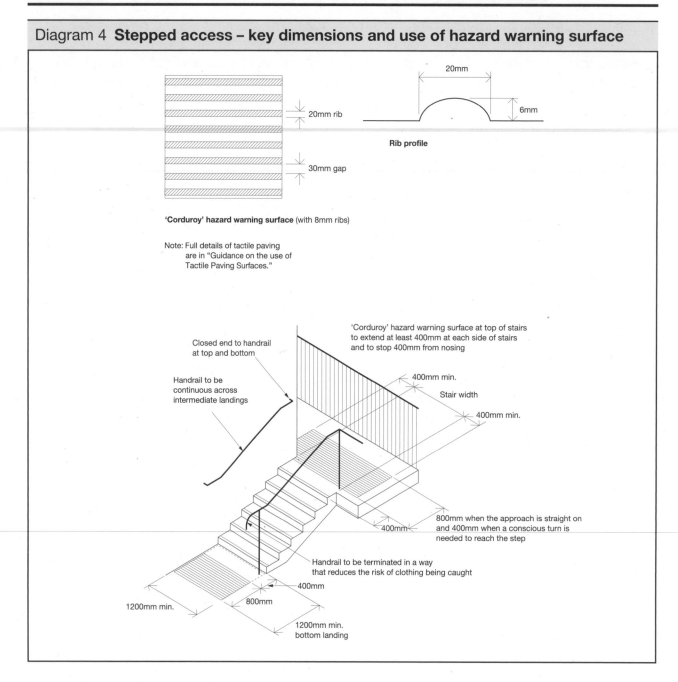

20mm

6mm

Rib profile

20mm rib

30mm gap

'Corduroy' hazard warning surface (with 8mm ribs)

Note: Full details of tactile paving are in "Guidance on the use of Tactile Paving Surfaces."

'Corduroy' hazard warning surface at top of stairs to extend at least 400mm at each side of stairs and to stop 400mm from nosing

Closed end to handrail at top and bottom

Handrail to be continuous across intermediate landings

400mm min.

Stair width

400mm min.

800mm when the approach is straight on and 400mm when a conscious turn is needed to reach the step

400mm

Handrail to be terminated in a way that reduces the risk of clothing being caught

400mm

800mm

1200mm min.

1200mm min. bottom landing

d. where there is side access onto an intermediate landing, a 'corduroy' hazard warning surface 400mm deep is provided either on the intermediate landing 400mm from both upper and lower flights, if there is sufficient space to accommodate the surface outside the line of the side access, or within the side access 400mm from the intermediate landing if there is a continuous handrail opposite the side access;

e. no doors swing across landings;

f. it has flights whose surface width between enclosing walls, strings or upstands is not less than 1.2m;

g. there are no single steps;

h. the rise of a flight between landings contains no more than 12 risers for a going of less than 350mm and no more than 18 risers for a going of 350mm or greater (see Diagram 5);

i. all nosings are made apparent by means of a permanently contrasting material 55mm wide on both the tread and the riser;

j. the projection of a step nosing over the tread below is avoided but, if necessary, not more than 25mm (see Diagram 6);

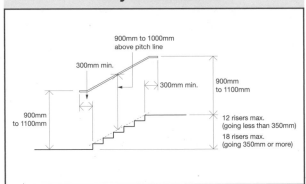

Diagram 5 **External steps and stairs – key dimensions**

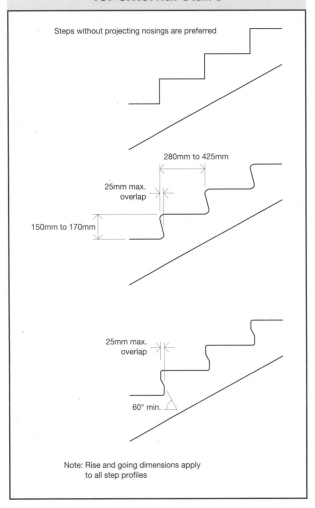

Diagram 6 **Examples of acceptable step profiles and key dimensions for external stairs**

Steps without projecting nosings are preferred

Note: Rise and going dimensions apply to all step profiles

k. the rise and going of each step is consistent throughout a flight;

l. the rise of each step is between 150mm and 170mm, except adjacent to existing buildings where, due to dimensional constraints, the case for a different rise is agreed with the building control body;

m. the going of each step is between 280mm and 425mm;

n. rises are not open;

o. there is a continuous handrail on each side of a flight and landings;

p. additional handrails divide the flight into channels not less than 1m wide and not more than 1.8m wide where the overall unobstructed width is more than 1.8m.

Note: In respect of 1.33(l) and (m), for school buildings, the preferred dimensions are a rise of 150mm, and a going of 280mm.

Handrails to external stepped and ramped access

Design considerations

1.34 People who have physical difficulty in negotiating changes of level need the help of a handrail that can be gripped easily, is comfortable to touch and, preferably, provides good forearm support.

1.35 Handrails should be spaced away from the wall and rigidly supported in a way that avoids impeding finger grip.

1.36 Handrails should be set at heights that are convenient for all users of the building and should extend safely beyond the top and bottom of a flight of steps, or a ramp, to give both stability and warning of the presence of a change in level. Consideration should be given to the provision of a second handrail on stairs in a wide range of building types, and particularly in schools, for use by children and people of short stature.

Provisions

1.37 Handrailing to external ramped and stepped access will satisfy Requirement M1 or M2 if:

a. the vertical height to the top of the upper handrail from the pitch line of the surface of a ramp, or a flight of steps, is between 900mm and 1000mm, and from the surface of a landing is between 900 and 1100mm (see Diagram 5);

b. where there is full height structural guarding, the vertical height to the top of a second lower handrail from the pitch line of the surface of a ramp, or a flight of steps, is 600mm, where provided;

c. it is continuous across the flights and landings of ramped or stepped access;

d. it extends at least 300mm horizontally beyond the top and bottom of a ramped access, or the top and bottom nosing of a flight or flights of steps, while not projecting into an access route;

e. it contrasts visually with the background against which it is seen, without being highly reflective;

f. its surface is slip resistant and not cold to the touch, in areas where resistance to vandalism or low maintenance are key factors, use of metals with relatively low thermal conductivity may be appropriate;

g. it terminates in a way that reduces the risk of clothing being caught;

h. its profile is either circular with a diameter of 32 and 50mm, or non-circular, 50mm wide and 39 mm deep having rounded edges with a radius a minimum of 15mm (see Diagram 7);

i. it protrudes no more than 100mm into the surface width of the ramped or stepped access where this would impinge on the stair width requirement of Part B1;

j. there is a clearance of between 60 and 75mm between the handrail and any adjacent wall surface;

k. there is a clearance of at least 50mm between a cranked support and the underside of the handrail;

l. its inner face is located no more than 50mm beyond the surface width of the ramped or stepped access.

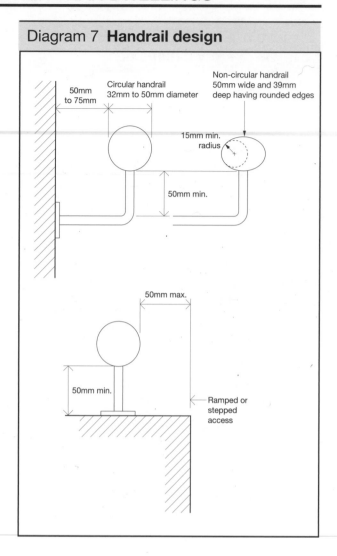

Diagram 7 **Handrail design**

Hazards on access routes

Design considerations

1.38 Features of a building that occasionally obstruct an access route, particularly if they are partially transparent and therefore indistinct, or cause a danger overhead, should not present a hazard to building users.

Provisions

1.39 Requirement M1 or M2 will be satisfied in relation to hazards on access routes where Approved Document K, sections 6 and 10 are complied with.

Note: Diagram 8 has been move to Approved Document K, Section 10, all other numbering remains the same

Section 2: Access into buildings other than dwellings

OBJECTIVES

2.1 The aim for all new buildings is for the principal entrance or entrances and any main staff entrance, and any lobbies, to be accessible.

2.2 Where it is not possible, e.g. in an existing building, for the principal or main staff entrance or entrances to be accessible, an alternative accessible entrance should be provided.

2.3 It is important to reduce the risks to people when entering the building.

Accessible entrances

Design considerations

2.4 Steeply sloping or restricted sites sometimes make it impossible for the principal or main staff entrance to be accessible, in which case an alternative accessible entrance may be necessary.

2.5 Accessible entrances should be clearly sign-posted and easily recognisable. Any structural elements, for example supports for a canopy, are useful in identifying the entrance, but should not present a hazard.

2.6 The route from the exterior across the threshold should provide weather protection, and not present a barrier for wheelchair users or a trip hazard for other people. A level threshold is preferred, especially for doors in frequent use.

Note: Guidance on sign-posting is given in BS 8300, Inclusive mobility and the Sign design guide.

Provisions

2.7 Accessible entrances will satisfy Requirement M1 or M2 if:

a. they are clearly sign-posted, incorporating the International Symbol of Access, from the edge of the site and from the principal entrance (if this is not accessible);

b. they are easily identified among the other elements of the building and the immediate environment, e.g. by lighting and/or visual contrast;

c. any structural supports at the entrance do not present a hazard for visually impaired people;

d. there is a level landing at least 1500 x 1500mm, clear of any door swings, immediately in front of the entrance and of a material that does not impede the movement of wheelchairs;

e. the threshold is level or, if a raised threshold is unavoidable, it has a total height of not more than 15mm, a minimum number of upstands and slopes, with any upstands higher than 5mm chamfered or rounded;

f. any door entry systems are accessible to deaf and hard of hearing people, and people who cannot speak;

g. weather protection is provided at manual non-powered entrance doors;

h. internal floor surfaces adjacent to the threshold are of materials that do not impede the movement of wheelchairs, e.g. not coir matting, and changes in floor materials do not create a potential trip hazard;

i. where mat wells are provided, the surface of the mat is level with the surface of the adjacent floor finish;

j. where provided as an alternative accessible entrance, an accessible internal route is provided to the spaces served by the principal or main staff entrances.

Doors to accessible entrances

Design considerations

2.8 Doors to the principal, or alternative accessible, entrance should be accessible to all, particularly wheelchair users and people with limited physical dexterity. Entrance doors may be manually operated without powered assistance, or power operated under manual or automatic control. Entrance doors should be capable of being held closed when not in use.

2.9   A non-powered manually operated entrance door, fitted with a self-closing device capable of closing the door against wind forces and the resistance of draught seals is unlikely to be openable by many people, particularly those who are wheelchair users or who have limited strength.

2.10   A powered door opening and closing system, either manually controlled or automatically operated by sensors, is the most satisfactory solution for most people. An automatic sliding door arrangement is particularly beneficial as it avoids the risks associated with automatic swing doors and its use can make it possible to reduce the length of any entrance lobby.

2.11   Once open, all doors to accessible entrances should be wide enough to allow unrestricted passage for a variety of users, including wheelchair users, people carrying luggage, people with assistance dogs, and parents with pushchairs and small children. It should be noted that double buggies are wider than wheelchairs and that, where relevant to the building type, this should be borne in mind when determining an appropriate effective clear width for an entrance door. There may be circumstances in existing buildings where it is not practicable or cost-effective to adopt the preferred effective clear widths for new buildings.

2.12   People should be able to see other people approaching from the opposite direction, thereby allowing sufficient reaction time for both parties to avoid a collision. Exceptions may be acceptable for reasons of privacy or security.

Provisions

2.13   Doors to accessible entrances will satisfy Requirement M1 or M2 if:

a. where required to be self-closing, a power-operated door opening and closing system is used when through calculation and experience it appears that it will not be possible otherwise for a person to open the door using a force not more than 30N at the leading edge from 0° (the door in the closed position)

to 30° open, and not more than 22.5N at the leading edge from 30° to 60° of the opening cycle;

b. the effective clear width through a single leaf door, or one leaf of a double leaf door, is in accordance with Table 2, and the rules for measurement are in accordance with Diagram 9;

c. they are installed in accordance with Approved Document K, section 10.

Table 2   Minimum effective clear widths of doors

Direction and width of approach	New buildings (mm)	Existing buildings (mm)
Straight-on (without a turn or oblique approach)	800	750
At right angles to an access route at least 1500mm wide	800	750
At right angles to an access route at least 1200mm wide	825	775
External doors to buildings used by the general public	1000	775

Note:

The effective clear width is the width of the opening measured at right angles to the wall in which the door is situated from the outside of the door stop on the door closing side to any obstruction on the hinge side, whether this be projecting door opening furniture, a weather board, the door or the door stop (see Diagram 9). For specific guidance on the effective clear widths of doors in sports accommodation, refer to 'Access for Disabled People'.

Diagram 9 **Effective clear width of doors**

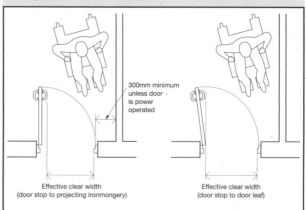

300mm minimum unless door is power operated

Effective clear width
(door stop to projecting ironmongery)

Effective clear width
(door stop to door leaf)

Manually operated non-powered entrance doors

Design considerations

2.14   Self-closing devices on manually operated non-powered swing doors disadvantage many people who have limited upper body strength, are pushing prams or are carrying heavy objects.

2.15 A space alongside the leading edge of a door should be provided to enable a wheelchair user to reach and grip the door handle, then open the door without releasing hold on the handle and without the footrest colliding with the return wall.

2.16 Door furniture on manually operated non-powered doors should be easy to operate by people with limited manual dexterity, and be readily apparent against the background of the door.

Provisions

2.17 Manually operated non-powered entrance doors will satisfy Requirement M1 or M2 if:

a. the opening force at the leading edge of the door is not more than 30N at the leading edge from 0° (the door in the closed position) to 30° open, and not more than 22.5N at the leading edge from 30° to 60° of the opening cycle;

b. there is an unobstructed space of at least 300mm on the pull side of the door between the leading edge of the door and any return wall, unless the door is a powered entrance door (see Diagram 9);

c. where fitted with a latch, the door opening furniture can be operated with one hand using a closed fist, e.g. a lever handle;

d. all door opening furniture contrasts visually with the surface of the door and is not cold to the touch.

Powered entrance doors

Design considerations

2.18 Activation (e.g. motion sensors and push buttons), safety features and the time-lapse allowed for entry and exit through powered door systems should be carefully considered to suit the needs of people who cannot react quickly.

2.19 Manual controls for powered entrance doors should be clearly distinguishable against the background and not located so that a person, having used the control,

needs to move to avoid contact with the door as it opens.

2.20 Revolving doors are not considered accessible. They create particular difficulties, and risk of injury, for people with assistance dogs, people with visual impairment or mobility problems and for parents with children and/or pushchairs. If a revolving door is used, an entrance door complying with 2.17 or 2.21 should be provided immediately adjacent to it and signed to show that it is accessible.

Provisions

2.21 Powered entrance doors will satisfy Requirement M1 or M2 if:

a. they have a sliding, swinging or folding action controlled:

   – manually by a push pad, card swipe, coded entry or remote control, or

   – automatically by a motion sensor or other proximity sensor, e.g. a contact mat;

b. when installed, automatic sensors are set so that automatically operated doors open early enough, and stay open long enough, to permit safe entry and exit;

c. when they are swing doors that open towards people approaching the doors, visual and audible warnings are provided to warn people of their automatic operation when both opening and shutting;

d. they incorporate a safety stop that is activated if the doors begin to close when a person is passing through;

e. they revert to manual control or fail safe in the open position in the event of a power failure;

f. when open, they do not project into any adjacent access route;

g. any manual controls for powered door systems are located between 750mm and 1000mm above floor level, operable with a closed fist and, when on the opening side of the door, are set back 1400mm from the leading edge of the door when fully open and contrast visually with the background against which they are seen.

Glass doors and glazed screens

Design considerations

2.22 People with visual impairment should be in no doubt as to the location of glass doors, especially when they are within a glazed screen. The choice of a different style of manifestation for the door and the glazed screen can help to differentiate between them.

2.23 The presence of the door should be apparent not only when it is shut but also when it is open. Where it can be held open, steps should be taken to avoid people being harmed by walking into the door.

Provisions

2.24 Glass doors and glazed screens will satisfy Requirement M1 or M2 if they comply with Approved Document K, Section 7.

Entrance lobbies

Design considerations

2.25 There are a number of reasons for providing a lobby:

- to limit air infiltration
- to maintain comfort by controlling draughts
- to increase security
- to provide transitional lighting.

2.26 The provision of a lobby may make it possible for an external door to have a self-closing device with a lower power size rating than might otherwise be the case. However, even in these circumstances, it may not be possible for the entrance door to meet the opening force criterion of 30N at the leading edge from 0° (the door in the closed position) to 30° open, and not more than 22.5N at the leading edge from 30° to 60° of the opening cycle (see 2.9).

2.27 The lobby should be large enough and of a shape to allow a wheelchair user or a person pushing a pram to move clear of one door before opening the second door. The lobby should also be capable of accommodating a companion helping a wheelchair user to open doors and guide the wheelchair through. The minimum length of the lobby is related to the chosen door size, the swing of each door, the projection of the door into the lobby and the size of an occupied wheelchair with a companion pushing. Where both doors of a lobby are automatic sliding doors, the length can be reduced as no door swings are involved, nor is space required for manual operation. Similarly, if 'reduced swing' door sets are used, the length can be reduced because the projection of the door into the lobby is reduced.

2.28 The aim should be to reduce potential hazards from local obstructions within the lobby and minimise distracting reflections from glazing. It is also desirable if rainwater from shoes or the wheels of wheelchairs is not taken into the building where it becomes a potential slip hazard, e.g. by the use of cleaning mats.

Provisions

2.29 Entrance lobbies will satisfy Requirement M1 or M2 if:

a. their length with single swing doors is in accordance with Diagram 10;

b. their length with double swing doors is at least (DP1 + DP2 + 1570mm);

c. their width (excluding any projections into the space) is at least 1200mm (or (DL1 or DL2) + 300mm) whichever is the greater when single leaf doors are used, and at least 1800mm when double leaf doors are used;

d. glazing within the lobby does not create distracting reflections;

e. floor surface materials within the lobby do not impede the movement of wheelchairs, e.g. not coir matting, and changes in floor materials do not create a potential trip hazard;

f. the floor surface helps to remove rainwater from shoes and wheelchairs;

g. where mat wells are provided, the surface of the mat is level with the surface of the adjacent floor finish;

h. any columns, ducts and similar full height elements that project into the lobby by more than 100mm are protected by a visually contrasting guard rail.

Diagram 10 Key dimensions for lobbies with single leaf doors

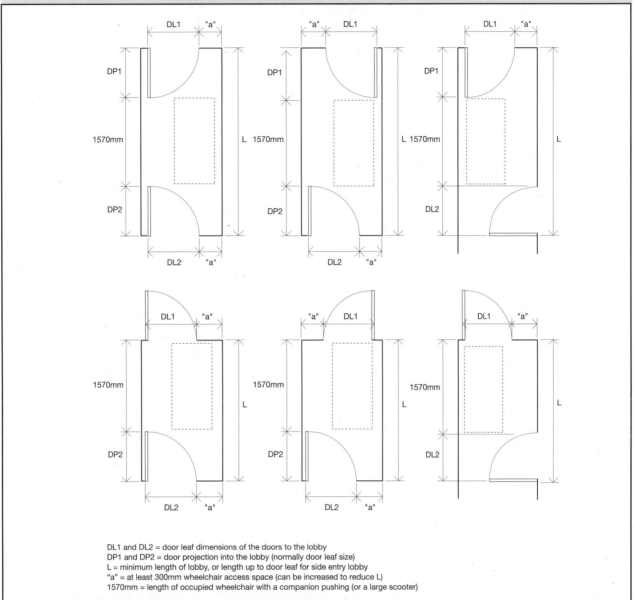

DL1 and DL2 = door leaf dimensions of the doors to the lobby
DP1 and DP2 = door projection into the lobby (normally door leaf size)
L = minimum length of lobby, or length up to door leaf for side entry lobby
"a" = at least 300mm wheelchair access space (can be increased to reduce L)
1570mm = length of occupied wheelchair with a companion pushing (or a large scooter)

NB: For every 100mm increase above 300mm in the dimension "a" (which gives a greater overlap of the wheelchair footprint over the door swing), there can be a corresponding reduction of 100mm in the dimension L, up to a maximum of 600mm reduction.

Section 3: Horizontal and vertical circulation in buildings other than dwellings

OBJECTIVE

3.1　The objective is for all people to travel vertically and horizontally within buildings conveniently and without discomfort in order to make use of all relevant facilities. This objective relates in the main, but not exclusively, to the provision of sufficient space for wheelchair manoeuvre and design features that make it possible for people to travel independently within buildings.

Entrance hall and reception area

Design considerations

3.2　As the entrance hall is the first point of contact with a building's activities and resources, the reception area in particular should not only be easily accessible but also convenient to use.

3.3　Where a service building has a reception or sales counter, there should be convenient access to it and part of it should be at a level suitable for a wheelchair user or a seated person. Any lower section should also be wheelchair-accessible on the reception side.

3.4　Designers should also be aware that glazed screens in front of the reception point, or light sources or reflective wall surfaces, such as glazed screens, located behind the reception point, could compromise the ability of a person with a hearing impairment to lip read or follow sign language.

3.5　It should be possible for information about the building to be easily obtained from a reception point or gathered from notice boards and signs.

Note: Guidance on aids to communication is available in BS 8300, and on the use of signs in the Sign design guide.

Provisions

3.6　An entrance hall and reception area will satisfy Requirement M1 or M2 if:

a. any reception point is located away from the principal entrance (while still providing a view of it) where there is a risk that external noise will be a problem;

b. any reception point is easily identifiable from the entrance doors or lobby, and the approach to it is direct and free from obstructions;

c. the design of the approach to any reception point allows space for wheelchair users to gain access to the reception point;

d. the clear manoeuvring space in front of any reception desk or counter is 1200mm deep and 1800mm wide if there is a knee recess at least 500mm deep, or 1400mm deep and 2200mm wide if there is no knee recess;

e. any reception desk or counter is designed to accommodate both standing and seated visitors such that at least one section of the counter is at least 1500mm wide, with its surface no higher than 760mm, and a knee recess, not less than 700mm, above floor level;

f. any reception point is provided with a hearing enhancement system, e.g. an induction loop;

g. the floor surface is slip resistant.

Internal doors

Design considerations

3.7　Since doors are potential barriers, their use should be avoided whenever appropriate. If doors are required, the use of self-closing devices should be minimised (particularly in parts of buildings used by the general public) since, as described in 2.14, they disadvantage many people who have limited upper body strength, are pushing prams or are carrying heavy objects. Where closing devices are needed for fire control, electrically powered hold-open devices or swing-free closing devices should be used as appropriate. These are devices whose closing mechanism is only activated in case of emergency. Low energy powered door systems may be used in locations not subject to frequent use or heavy traffic as the opening and closing action is relatively slow.

3.8 The presence of doors, whether open or closed, should be apparent to visually impaired people through the careful choice of colour and material for the door and its surroundings. For example, when a door is open, people with impaired sight should be able to identify the door opening within the wall, as well as the leading edge of the door.

3.9 Other design considerations for internal doors are as set out in 2.14 to 2.16 under 'Manually operated non-powered entrance doors' and should be referred to for guidance.

Note: Guidance is available in BS 8300 on:

– electrically powered hold-open devices

– swing-free systems

– low energy powered door systems.

Provisions

3.10 Internal doors will satisfy Requirement M1 or M2 if:

a. where needing to be opened manually, the opening force at the leading edge of the door is not more than 30N from 0° (the door in the closed position) to 30° open, and not more than 22.5N from 30° to 60° of the opening cycle;

b. the effective clear width through a single leaf door, or one leaf of a double leaf door, is in accordance with Table 2 and Diagram 9;

c. there is an unobstructed space of at least 300mm on the pull side of the door between the leading edge of the door and any return wall, unless the door has power-controlled opening or it provides access to a standard hotel bedroom;

d. where fitted with a latch, the door opening furniture can be operated with one hand using a closed fist, e.g. a lever handle;

e. all door opening furniture contrasts visually with the surface of the door;

f. the door frames contrast visually with the surrounding wall;

g. the surface of the leading edge of any door that is not self-closing, or is likely to be held open, contrasts visually with the other door surfaces and its surroundings;

h. where appropriate in door leaves or side panels wider than 450mm, vision panels towards the leading edge of the door have vertical dimensions which include at least the minimum zone, or zones, of visibility between 500mm and 1500mm from the floor, if necessary interrupted between 800mm and 1150mm above the floor, e.g. to accommodate an intermediate horizontal rail (see Approved Document K, Section 10);

i. when of glass, they are clearly defined with manifestation on the glass that complies with Approved Document K, section 7;

j. when of glass or fully glazed, they are clearly differentiated from any adjacent glazed wall or partition by the provision of a high-contrast strip at the top and on both sides;

k. fire doors, particularly those in corridors, are held open with an electro-magnetic device, but self-close when:

– activated by smoke detectors linked to the door individually, or to a main fire/smoke alarm system;

– the power supply fails;

– activated by a hand-operated switch;

l. fire doors, particularly to individual rooms, are fitted with swing-free devices that close when activated by smoke detectors or the building's fire alarm system, or when the power supply fails;

m. any low energy powered swing door system is capable of being operated in manual mode, in powered mode or in power-assisted mode.

Corridors and passageways

Design considerations

3.11 Corridors and passageways should be wide enough to allow people with buggies, people carrying cases or people on crutches to pass others on the access route. Wheelchair users should also have access to adjacent rooms and spaces, be able to pass other people and, where necessary, turn through 180°. Corridors narrower than indicated in this guidance, or localised narrowing (e.g. at archways), might be reasonable in some locations, such as in existing buildings or in some extensions.

3.12 In order to help people with visual impairment to appreciate the size of a space they have entered, or to find their way around, there should be a visual contrast between the wall and the ceiling, and between the wall and the floor. Such attention to surface finishes should be coupled with good natural and artificial lighting design.

3.13 Good acoustic design should be employed to achieve an acoustic environment that is neither too reverberant nor too absorbent so that announcements and conversations can be heard clearly.

Provisions

3.14 Corridors and passageways will satisfy Requirement M1 or M2 if:

a. elements such as columns, radiators and fire hoses do not project into the corridor, or where this is unavoidable, a means of directing people around them, such as a visually contrasting guard rail, is provided;

b. they have an unobstructed width (excluding any projections into the space) along their length of at least 1200mm;

c. where they have an unobstructed width of less than 1800mm, they have passing places at least 1800mm long and with an unobstructed width of at least 1800mm at reasonable intervals, e.g. at corridor junctions, to allow wheelchair users to pass each other;

d. the floor is level or predominantly level (with a gradient no steeper than 1:60), with any section with a gradient of 1:20 or steeper designed as an internal ramp and in accordance with Table 1 and Diagram 3;

e. where a section of the floor has a gradient, in the direction of travel, steeper than 1:60, but less steep than 1:20, it rises no more than 500mm without a level rest area at least 1500mm long (with a gradient no steeper than 1:60);

f. any sloping section extends the full width of the corridor or, if not, the exposed edge is clearly identified by visual contrast and, where necessary, protected by guarding;

g. any door opening towards a corridor, which is a major access route or an escape route, should be recessed so that, when fully open, it does not project into the corridor space, except where the doors are to minor utility facilities, such as small store rooms and locked duct cupboards;

h. any door from a unisex wheelchair-accessible toilet projects when open into a corridor that is not a major access route or an escape route, provided the corridor is at least 1800mm wide at that point;

i. on a major access route or an escape route, the wider leaf of a series of double doors with leaves of unequal width is on the same side of the corridor throughout the length of the corridor;

j. floor surface finishes with patterns that could be mistaken for steps or changes of level are avoided;

k. floor finishes are slip resistant;

l. any glazed screens alongside a corridor are clearly defined with manifestation on the glass that complies with Approved Document K, section 7.

Note: In respect of 3.14(b), for school buildings, the preferred corridor width dimension is 2700mm where there are lockers within the corridor.

Internal lobbies

Design considerations

3.15 An internal lobby should allow a wheelchair user, with or without a companion, or a person pushing a pram or buggy to move clear of one door before attempting to open the second door, as indicated in 2.27, under 'External lobbies'.

Provisions

3.16 Internal lobbies will satisfy Requirement M1 or M2 if:

a. their length with single swing doors is in accordance with Diagram 10;

b. their length with double swing doors is at least (DP1 + DP2 + 1570mm);

c. their width (excluding any projections into the space) is at least 1200mm (or (DL1 or DL2) + 300mm) whichever is the greater when single leaf doors are used, and at least 1800mm when double leaf doors are used;

d. glazing within the lobby does not create distracting reflections;

e. any junctions of floor surface materials at the entrance to the lobby area do not create a potential trip hazard;

f. any columns, ducts and similar full height elements that project into the lobby by more than 100mm are protected by a visually contrasting guard rail.

Vertical circulation within the building

Design considerations

3.17 A passenger lift is the most suitable means of vertical access and should be provided wherever possible. However, given the space constraints in some buildings, it may not always be possible to install the type and size of passenger lift that would be suitable for use by all, and other options may need to be considered to provide for users with mobility impairments.

3.18 Signs indicating the location of a lifting device accessible by mobility-impaired people should be clearly visible from the building entrance. Additionally, a sign identifying the floor reached should be provided on each landing in a location that can be easily seen from the lifting device and is designed so that it contrasts visually with its surrounding.

3.19 Whatever lifting device is chosen, internal stairs should always be provided as an alternative means of vertical access, and designed to suit ambulant disabled people and those with impaired sight.

3.20 A ramp may also be provided on an internal circulation route to a suitable lifting device, if a change of level is unavoidable.

Provision of lifting devices

Design considerations

3.21 For all buildings, a passenger lift is the most suitable form of access for people moving from one storey to another.

3.22 For existing buildings, and in exceptional circumstances for new developments with particular constraints (e.g. a listed building or an infill site in a historic town centre), where a passenger lift cannot be accommodated, a vertical lifting platform (platform lift), although not equivalent to a passenger lift, may be considered as an alternative option to provide access for persons with impaired mobility.

3.23 In exceptional circumstances in an existing building, a wheelchair platform stairlift may be considered, provided its installation does not conflict with requirements for means of escape.

Provisions

3.24 The provision of lifting devices will satisfy Requirement M1 or M2 if:

a. new developments have a passenger lift serving all storeys;

b. new developments, where due to site constraints a passenger lift cannot be accommodated to provide access to persons with impaired mobility, have a lifting platform, of a type designed for the vertical height to be travelled;

c. existing buildings have a passenger lift serving all storeys or, if a passenger lift cannot reasonably be accommodated to provide access to persons with impaired mobility, they have a lifting platform, of a type designed for the vertical height to be travelled;

d. existing buildings have a wheelchair platform stairlift serving an intermediate level or a single storey, only in exceptional circumstances.

General requirements for lifting devices

Design considerations

3.25 In selecting the appropriate lifting device care should be taken to ensure it is fit for purpose. Relevant legislation includes the Lift Regulations 1997 SI 1997/831, the Lifting Operations and Lifting Equipment Regulations 1998 SI 1998/2307, the Provision and Use of Work Equipment Regulations 1998 SI 1998/2306 and the Management of Health and Safety at Work Regulations 1999 SI 1999/3242.

3.26 The illumination in the passenger lift car, on the lifting platform or on the wheelchair platform stairlift should minimise glare, reflection, confusing shadows or pools of light and dark.

3.27 All users including wheelchair users should be able to reach and use the controls that summon and direct the lifting device.

Note: Further guidance is available in BS 8300.

Provisions

3.28 The installation of lifting devices will satisfy Requirement M1 or M2 if:

a. there is an unobstructed manoeuvring space of 1500mm x 1500mm, or a straight access route 900mm wide, in front of each lifting device;

b. the landing call buttons are located between 900mm and 1100mm from the floor of the landing and at least 500mm from any return wall;

c. the landing call button symbols, where provided, and lifting device control button symbols are raised to facilitate tactile reading;

d. all call and control buttons contrast visually with the surrounding face plate, and the face plate similarly contrasts with the surface on which it is mounted;

e. the floor of the lifting device should not be of a dark colour and should have frictional qualities similar to, or higher than, the floor of the landing;

f. a handrail is provided on at least one wall of the lifting device with its top surface at 900mm (nominal) above the floor and located so that it does not obstruct the controls or the mirror;

g. a suitable emergency communication system is fitted.

Passenger lifts

Design considerations

3.29 A wheelchair user needs sufficient space and time to enter and leave a passenger lift, particularly when sharing it with other people. Lift sizes should therefore be chosen to suit the anticipated density of use of the building and the needs of disabled people. The minimum size lift car shown in the provisions below accommodates a wheelchair user with an accompanying person. A larger lift size (2000mm wide by 1400mm deep) will accommodate any type of wheelchair together with several other passengers. It will also allow a wheelchair user or a person with a walking frame to turn through 180°.

3.30 Lift door systems should be designed to allow adequate time for people, and any assistance dogs, to enter or leave the lift without coming into contact with closing doors.

3.31 People using or waiting for a lift need audible and visual information to tell them that a lift has arrived, which floor it has reached and where in a bank of lifts it is located.

3.32 The use of visually and acoustically reflective wall surfaces can cause discomfort for people with visual and hearing impairment.

3.33 Where planning allows, lift cars (used for access between two levels only) may be provided with opposing doors to allow a wheelchair user to leave without reversing out.

Provisions

3.34 Passenger lifts will satisfy Requirement M1 or M2 if:

a. they conform to the requirements of the Lift Regulations 1997, SI 1997/831 (**Note:** These regulations may be met by compliance with, among other things, the relevant British Standards, EN 81 series of standards, in particular BS EN 81-70:2003 Safety rules for the construction and installation of lifts. Particular applications for passenger and good passenger lifts, or, where necessary, by product certification issued by a Notified Body);

b. they are accessible from the remainder of the storey;

c. the minimum dimensions of the lift cars are 1100mm wide and 1400mm deep (see Diagram 11);

d. for lifts of a size that does not allow a wheelchair user to turn around within the lift car, a mirror is provided in the lift car to enable a wheelchair user to see the space behind the wheelchair;

e. power-operated horizontal sliding doors provide an effective clear width of at least 800mm (nominal);

f. doors are fitted with timing devices and re-opening activators to allow adequate time for people and any assistance dogs to enter or leave;

g. car controls are located between 900mm and 1200mm (preferably 1100mm) from the car floor and at least 400mm from any return wall;

h. landing call buttons are located between 900mm and 1100mm from the floor of the landing and at least 500mm from any return wall;

i. lift landing and car doors are distinguishable visually from the adjoining walls;

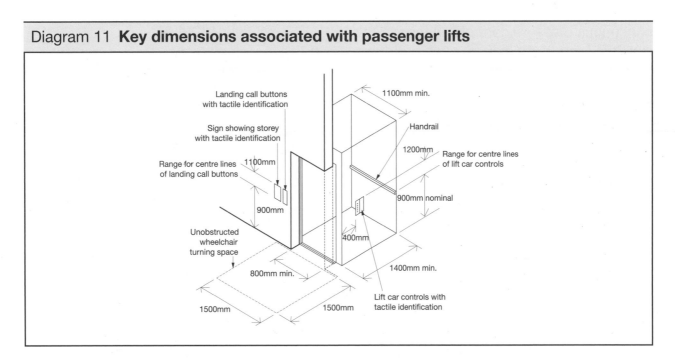

Diagram 11 **Key dimensions associated with passenger lifts**

Landing call buttons with tactile identification

1100mm min.

Sign showing storey with tactile identification

Handrail

Range for centre lines of landing call buttons — 1100mm

1200mm

Range for centre lines of lift car controls

900mm nominal

900mm

Unobstructed wheelchair turning space

400mm

800mm min.

1400mm min.

1500mm

1500mm

Lift car controls with tactile identification

j. audible and visual indication of lift arrival and location is provided in the lift car and the lift lobby;

k. areas of glass are identifiable by people with impaired vision;

l. where the lift is to be used to evacuate disabled people in an emergency, it conforms to the relevant recommendations of BS 5588-8.

Lifting platforms

Design considerations

3.35 A lifting platform should only be provided to transfer wheelchair users, people with impaired mobility and their companions vertically between levels or storeys.

3.36 All users including wheelchair users should be able to reach and use the controls that summon and direct the lifting platform.

3.37 People using or waiting for a lifting platform need audible and visual information to tell them that the platform has arrived, and which floor it has reached.

3.38 Lifting platforms travel slowly between landings and may not be suitable for lone users with certain disabilities, e.g. those easily fatigued.

3.39 Lifting platforms are operated by continuous pressure controls. In their simplest form these may be push buttons. However, another means of continuous pressure control may need to be considered to accommodate the needs of users with varying degrees of manual dexterity.

3.40 It is important when selecting a lifting platform that due care and attention is paid to its intended use particularly if located in an unsupervised environment. Where management control cannot be exercised, particular attention should be paid to the product's designed duty cycle.

3.41 Where planning allows, lifting platforms may be provided with opposing doors when used for access between two levels only, to allow a wheelchair user to leave without reversing out. In some cases, it may be more convenient to provide a second door at 90° to the first, in which case a wider platform would be required.

3.42 The use of visually and acoustically reflective wall surfaces should be minimised within the lifting platform to prevent discomfort for people with visual and hearing impairment.

Provisions

3.43 Lifting platforms will satisfy Requirement M1 or M2 if:

a. they conform to the requirements of the Supply of Machinery (Safety) Regulations 1992, SI 1992/3073 (**Note:** These regulations may be met by compliance, among other things, with the relevant British Standards, EN81 series of standards or, where necessary, by product certification issued by a Notified Body. In the absence of relevant harmonised European Standards, products with a travel exceeding 3m must have a product certificate issued by a Notified Body);

b. the vertical travel distance is:

  i. not more than 2m, where there is no liftway enclosure and no floor penetration;

  ii. more than 2m, where there is a liftway enclosure;

c. the rated speed of the platform does not exceed 0.15m/s;

d. lifting platform controls are located between 800mm and 1100mm from the floor of the lifting platform and at least 400mm from any return wall;

e. continuous pressure controls are provided;

f. landing call buttons are located between 900mm and 1100mm from the floor of the landing and at least 500mm from any return wall;

g. the minimum clear dimensions of the platform are:

  i. 800mm wide and 1250mm deep, where the lifting platform is not enclosed and where provision is being made for an unaccompanied wheelchair user;

ii. 900mm wide and 1400mm deep, where the lifting platform is enclosed and where provision is being made for an unaccompanied wheelchair user;

iii. 1100mm wide and 1400mm deep where two doors are located at 90° relative to each other and where the lifting platform is enclosed or where provision is being made for an accompanied wheelchair user;

h. doors have an effective clear width of at least 900mm for an 1100mm wide and 1400mm deep lifting platform and at least 800mm in other cases;

i. they are fitted with clear instructions for use;

j. the lifting platform entrances are accessible from the remainder of the storey;

k. doors are distinguishable visually from the adjoining walls;

l. an audible and visual announcement of platform arrival and level reached is provided;

m. areas of glass are identifiable by people with impaired vision.

Wheelchair platform stairlifts

Design considerations

3.44 Wheelchair platform stairlifts are only intended for the transportation of wheelchair users and should only be considered for conversions and alterations where it is not practicable to install a conventional passenger lift or a lifting platform. Such stairlifts travel up the string of a stair. They should not be installed where their operation restricts the safe use of the stair by other people.

3.45 A wheelchair platform stairlift allows a wheelchair user to travel independently up and down stairs while remaining seated in a wheelchair. A wheelchair platform stairlift may be more suitable for use in small areas with a unique function, e.g. a small library gallery, a staff rest room or a training room.

3.46 Wheelchair platform stairlifts travel slowly between landings and may not be suitable for users with certain disabilities, e.g. those easily fatigued.

3.47 Wheelchair platform stairlifts are operated by continuous pressure controls, commonly a joystick. However, another means of continuous pressure control may need to be considered to accommodate users with varying degrees of manual dexterity.

3.48 Wheelchair platform stairlifts are only suitable where users can be instructed in their safe use and where management supervision can be ensured.

Provisions

3.49 Wheelchair platform stairlifts will satisfy Requirement M1 or M2 if

a. they conform to the requirements of the Supply of Machinery (Safety) Regulations 1992, SI 1992/3073 (**Note:** These regulations may be met by compliance, among other things, with the relevant British Standards, EN81 series of standards or where necessary Notified Body approval);

b. in a building with a single stairway, the required clear width of the flight of stairs and landings for means of escape is maintained when the wheelchair platform is in the parked position (see also Approved Document B);

c. the rated speed of the platform does not exceed 0.15m/s;

d. continuous pressure controls are provided;

e. the minimum clear dimensions of the platform are 800mm wide and 1250mm deep;

f. they are fitted with clear instructions for use;

g. access with an effective clear width of at least 800mm is provided;

h. controls are designed to prevent unauthorised use.

Internal stairs

Design considerations

3.50 With the exception of the need for hazard warning surfaces on landings, other design considerations for internal stairs are as those for 'Stepped access' (see 1.29 to 1.32). It is not reasonable to require a hazard warning surface at the head of internal stairs since there is no recognised warning surface for use internally which can be guaranteed not to constitute a trip hazard when used alongside flooring surfaces with different frictional resistance characteristics. However, designers should be aware of the potential risk of having a stair directly in line with an access route. For mobility-impaired people, a going of at least 300mm is preferred.

Provisions

3.51 Internal stairs will satisfy Requirement M1 or M2 if they comply with Approved Document K, section 1.

Note: Diagram 12 has been move to Approved Document K, Section 1, all other numbering remains the same

Internal ramps

Design considerations

3.52 With the exception of issues relating specifically to the external environment, the design considerations for internal ramps are as those for 'Ramped access' (see 1.19 to 1.25). It is worth reiterating that ramps are not necessarily safe and convenient for ambulant disabled people. For example, some people who can walk but have restricted mobility find it more difficult to negotiate a ramp than a stair. Unless, therefore, a ramp is short, has a shallow gradient and the rise is no more than the minimum that can be provided by two risers, steps should be provided as well as a ramp.

Provisions

3.53 Internal ramps will satisfy Requirement M1 or M2 if they comply with Approved Document K, section 2.

Handrails to internal steps, stairs and ramps

Design considerations

3.54 The design considerations for handrails are as those for 'Handrails to external stepped and ramped access' in 1.34 to 1.36.

Provisions

3.55 Handrails to internal steps, stairs and ramps will satisfy Requirement M1 or M2 if they comply with Approved Document K, sections 1–3.

Section 4: Facilities in buildings other than dwellings

OBJECTIVES

4.1 The aim is for all people to have access to, and the use of, all the facilities provided within buildings. They should also be able to participate in the proceedings at lecture/conference facilities and at entertainment or leisure and social venues, not only as spectators, but also as participants and/or staff.

4.2 Where permanent or removable seating is provided as part of the design, allowance should be made for disabled people to have a choice of seating location at spectator events. It should also be possible for them to have a clear view of the activity taking place while not obstructing the view of others.

4.3 In refreshment facilities, bars and counters (or sections of them) should be at a level suitable for wheelchair users. All floor areas, even when located at different levels, should be accessible.

4.4 A proportion of the sleeping accommodation in hotels, motels and student accommodation should be designed for independent use by wheelchair users. The remainder should include facilities that make them suitable for people who do not use a wheelchair, but may have mobility, sensory, dexterity or learning difficulties.

Audience and spectator facilities

Design considerations

4.5 Audience and spectator facilities fall primarily into three categories:

a. lecture/conference facilities

b. entertainment facilities (e.g. theatres/cinemas)

c. sports facilities (e.g. stadia).

Note: The guidance here relates mainly to seating. For guidance on reception and sales counters, refer to 3.2 to 3.5.

Audience facilities generally

4.6 Wheelchair users and those with mobility or sensory impairment may need to view or listen from a particular side, or sit in the front for lip reading or to read sign interpreters. They should be provided with spaces into which they can manoeuvre easily, and which offer them a clear view of an event, while ensuring they are not segregated into special areas. Wheelchair users, people who have difficulty in using seats with fixed arms and those with assistance dogs should also have the choice of sitting next to a conventionally seated person or a companion wheelchair user. Consideration should be given to providing an area next to certain seats for an assistance dog to rest. By having some removable seating at the front and back of blocks of seats (possibly in complete rows), greater flexibility in location can be achieved and a greater number of wheelchair users than the minimum provision shown in Table 3 can be accommodated.

4.7 Greater spacing between rows of seats at the rear of a block of seating, or at the end of rows, may provide extra legroom for people of large stature. With several seats removed, these locations may also be suitable for wheelchair users. It is desirable for seating to contrast visually with the surroundings.

4.8 All users of facilities should be able to locate suitable seating and move safely and easily to and from the seating area and ancillary accommodation, such as lavatories, dining rooms and bedroom suites.

Lecture/conference facilities

4.9 People with hearing impairments should be able to participate fully in conferences, committee meetings and study groups. All people should be able to use presentation facilities. Consideration should be given to good sight lines and the design and location of lecture equipment (demonstration table, lectern, projection screen) to ensure that patterned walls, poor interior lighting or very bright natural back-lighting does not have a detrimental effect on the ability of people to receive information from a sign language interpreter or a lip speaker (see 4.32 to 4.34).

Entertainment, leisure and social facilities

4.10 In facilities for entertainment, e.g. theatres and cinemas, it is normal for seating to be more closely packed than in other types of auditoria. Care is needed in the design and location of wheelchair spaces so that all visitors can enjoy the atmosphere. Reference should also be made to Technical standard for places of entertainment.

Sports facilities

4.11 For guidance on integrating the needs of disabled people into the design of spectator facilities, in particular the provision of, and access to, suitable spaces for wheelchair users in stadia, see Guide to safety at sports grounds, Accessible stadia: a good practice guide to the design of facilities to meet the needs of disabled spectators and other users and Access for disabled people.

Provisions

4.12 Audience and spectator facilities will satisfy Requirement M1 if:

For audience seating generally

a. the route to wheelchair spaces is accessible by wheelchair users;

b. stepped access routes to audience seating are provided with fixed handrails (see 1.34 to 1.37 for details of handrails);

c. the minimum number of permanent and removable spaces provided for wheelchair users is in accordance with Table 3;

Table 3	**Provision of wheelchair space in audience seating**	
Seating capacity	**Minimum provision of spaces for wheelchairs**	
	Permanent	Removable
Up to 600	1% of total seating capacity (rounded up)	Remainder to make a total of 6
Over 600 but less than 10,000	1% of total seating capacity (rounded up)	Additional provision, if desired

Note:

For seating capacities of 10,000 or more, guidance is given in 'Accessible stadia: a good practice guide to the design of facilities to meet the needs of disabled spectators and other users'.

d. some wheelchair spaces (whether permanent or created by removing seats) are provided in pairs, with standard seating on at least one side (see Diagram 13);

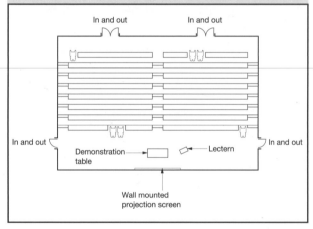

Diagram 13 **An example of wheelchair spaces in a lecture theatre**

e. where more than two wheelchair spaces are provided, they are located to give a range of views of the event at each side, as well as at the front and back of the seating area;

f. the minimum clear space provided for access to wheelchair spaces is 900mm;

g. the clear space allowance for an occupied wheelchair in a parked position is 900mm wide by 1400mm deep;

h. the floor of each wheelchair space is horizontal;

i.   some seats are located so that an assistance dog can accompany its owner and rest in front of, or under, the seat;

j.   standard seats at the ends of rows and next to wheelchair spaces have detachable, or lift-up, arms;

For seating on a stepped terraced floor

k.   wheelchair spaces at the back of a stepped terraced floor are provided in accordance with Diagram 14 or 15, the arrangement in Diagram 15 being particularly suitable for entertainment buildings, such as theatres or cinemas, subject to the approval of the licensing authority;

For lecture/conference facilities

l.   where a podium or stage is provided, wheelchair users have access to it by means of a ramp or lifting platform;

m. a hearing enhancement system in accordance with 4.36 is provided for people with impaired hearing.

Refreshment facilities

Design considerations

4.13 Refreshment facilities, such as restaurants and bars, should be designed so that they can be reached and used by all people independently or with companions. Staff areas should also be accessible.

4.14 All public areas, including lavatory accommodation, public telephones and external terraces should be accessible. Where premises contain self-service and waiter service, all patrons should have access to both.

4.15 In many refreshment facilities, changes in level are used to differentiate between different functions or to create a certain atmosphere through interior design. Changes of floor level are acceptable provided the different levels are accessible.

Provisions

4.16 Refreshment facilities will satisfy Requirement M1 if:

a.   all users have access to all parts of the facility;

b.   part of the working surface of a bar or serving counter is permanently accessible to wheelchair users, and at a level of not more than 850mm above the floor and, where necessary, part at a higher level for people standing;

c.   the worktop of a shared refreshment facility (e.g. for tea making) is at 850mm above the floor with a clear space beneath at least 700mm above the floor (see Diagram 16) and the delivery of water complies with 5.4(a) and (b);

d.   a wheelchair-accessible threshold (see 2.7(e)) is located at the transition between an external seating area and the interior of the facility.

Diagram 14 Possible location of wheelchair spaces in front of a rear aisle

Steps

1100mm*

Aisle dimension

1400mm x 900mm nominal wheelchair spaces

More seats can be removed if necessary to create more wheelchair space

Rear wall

* Dimension derived from BS 8300

Diagram 15 An example of wheelchair space provision in a cinema or theatre

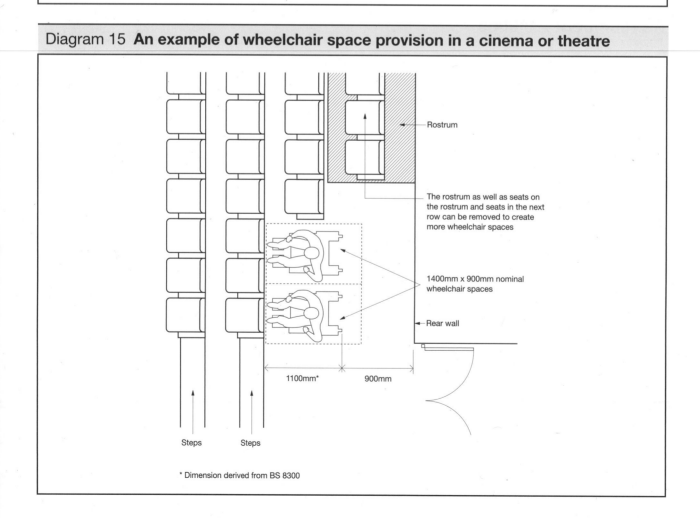

Rostrum

The rostrum as well as seats on the rostrum and seats in the next row can be removed to create more wheelchair spaces

1400mm x 900mm nominal wheelchair spaces

Rear wall

1100mm*

900mm

Steps   Steps

* Dimension derived from BS 8300

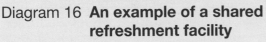

Diagram 16 **An example of a shared refreshment facility**

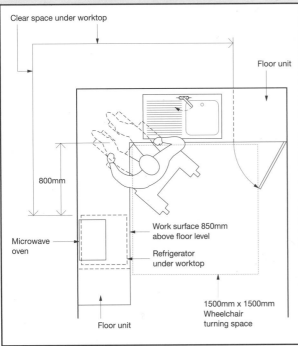

Clear space under worktop

Floor unit

800mm

Microwave oven

Work surface 850mm above floor level

Refrigerator under worktop

Floor unit

1500mm x 1500mm Wheelchair turning space

Sleeping accommodation

Design considerations

4.17 Sleeping accommodation, where provided for a significant number of people, e.g. in hotels, motels and student accommodation, should aim to be convenient for all. People who use wheelchairs are likely to require greater provision of space and access to en-suite sanitary accommodation. A proportion of rooms will, therefore, need to accommodate wheelchair users. In student accommodation, it is beneficial to have a wheelchair-accessible toilet available for use by disabled visitors.

4.18 Wheelchair users should be able to reach all the facilities available within the building. In general, accessible bedrooms should be no less advantageously situated than other bedrooms. It would be beneficial if entrance doors to wheelchair-accessible bedrooms were powered opening, as this could avoid the need for the 300mm access space adjacent to the leading edge of the door.

4.19 Wheelchair-accessible bedrooms should be sufficiently spacious to enable a wheelchair user to transfer to one side of a bed, with or without assistance. Wheelchair users should be able to manoeuvre around and use the facilities in the room, and operate switches and controls. They should also be able to gain access to and conveniently use sanitary accommodation and, where provided, balconies. En-suite sanitary facilities are the preferred option for wheelchair-accessible bedrooms. Unless there are compelling reasons for not doing so, there should be at least as many en-suite shower rooms as en-suite bathrooms, as mobility-impaired people may find it easier to use a shower than a bath. An en-suite shower room or bathroom would benefit from having a finger rinse basin adjacent to the WC, as well as a wash basin or basin in a vanity unit.

4.20 It is also important to ensure that, in all bedrooms, built-in wardrobes and shelving are accessible and convenient to use. It is an advantage if curtains and blinds are provided with automatic or other remotely controlled opening devices such as rods or pull cords.

4.21 Wheelchair users should also be able to visit companions in other bedrooms, for example when attending conferences or when on holiday with their families. In these instances, bedrooms not designed for independent use by a person in a wheelchair need to have the outer door wide enough to be accessible to a wheelchair user.

4.22 For a proportion of wheelchair-accessible bedrooms, it would be useful to provide a connecting door to an adjacent bedroom for a companion.

4.23 For people with limited manual dexterity, electronic card-activated locks for bedroom entrance doors and lever taps in sanitary accommodation can be an advantage.

Provisions

4.24 Sleeping accommodation will satisfy Requirement M1 if:

For all bedrooms

a. the effective clear width of the door from the access corridor complies with Table 2;

b. swing doors, where provided for built-in wardrobes and other storage systems, open through 180°;

c. handles on hinged and sliding doors are easy to grip and operate and contrast visually with the surface of the door;

d. openable windows and window controls are located between 800 and 1000mm above the floor and are easy to operate without using both hands simultaneously;

e. all bedrooms have a visual fire alarm signal, in addition to the requirements of Part B;

f. any room numbers are indicated in embossed characters;

For wheelchair-accessible bedrooms

g. at least one wheelchair-accessible bedroom is provided for every 20 bedrooms, or part thereof;

h. wheelchair-accessible bedrooms are located on accessible routes that lead to all other available facilities within the building;

i. wheelchair-accessible bedrooms are designed to provide a choice of location and have a standard of amenity equivalent to that of other bedrooms;

j. the door from the access corridor to a wheelchair-accessible bedroom complies with the relevant provisions of 'Internal doors' (see 3.10), in particular the maximum permissible opening force, Table 2 and the need for a clear space of 300mm from the leading edge of the door to the side wall;

k. the effective clear width of any door to an en-suite bathroom or shower room within the wheelchair-accessible bedroom complies with Table 2;

l. the size of wheelchair-accessible bedrooms allows for a wheelchair user to manoeuvre at the side of a bed, then transfer independently to it. An example of a wheelchair-accessible bedroom layout is shown in Diagram 17;

m. sanitary facilities, en-suite to a wheelchair-accessible bedroom, comply with the provisions of 5.15 to 5.21 for 'Wheelchair-accessible bathrooms' or 'Wheelchair-accessible shower facilities';

n. wide angle viewers, where provided in the entrance door to a wheelchair-accessible bedroom, are located at 1050mm and 1500mm above floor level, to enable viewing by people who are seated or standing;

o. a balcony, where provided to a wheelchair-accessible bedroom, has a door whose effective clear width complies with Table 2, has a level threshold and has no horizontal transoms between 900mm and 1200mm above the floor;

p. there are no permanent obstructions in a zone 1500mm back from any balcony doors;

q. an emergency assistance alarm (together with a reset button) is located in a wheelchair-accessible bedroom and activated by a pull cord, sited so that it can be operated both from the bed and from an adjacent floor area;

r. an emergency assistance call signal outside an accessible bedroom is located so that it can be easily seen and heard by those able to give assistance and, in any case, at a central control point.

Switches, outlets and controls

Design considerations

4.25 The key factors that affect the use of switches, outlets and controls are ease of operation, visibility, height and freedom from obstruction. However, there will be exceptions to height requirements for some outlets, e.g. those set into the floor in open plan offices.

Diagram 17 **One example of a wheelchair-accessible hotel bedroom with en-suite sanitary facilities**

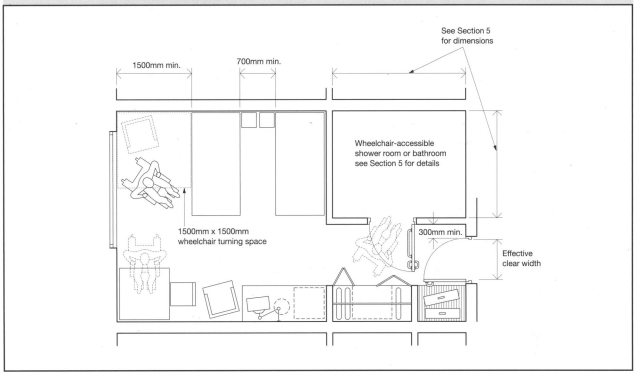

4.26 A consistent relationship with doorways and corners will further reinforce the ease with which people manipulate switches and controls.

4.27 All users should be able to locate a control, know which setting it is on and use it without inadvertently changing its setting.

4.28 Controls that contrast visually with their surroundings are more convenient for visually impaired people, as are light switches that are activated by a large push pad. The colours red and green should not be used in combination as indicators of 'on' and 'off' for switches and controls. It may be useful to use text or a pictogram to clarify the purpose and status of multiple switches and controls.

4.29 It is also an advantage if individual switches on panels and on multiple socket outlets are well separated, or in the form of large touch plates, to avoid the inadvertent selection of an adjacent control by visually impaired people and people with limited dexterity.

Provisions

4.30 Switches, outlets and controls will satisfy Requirement M1 if:

a. wall-mounted socket outlets, telephone points and TV sockets are located between 400mm and 1000mm above the floor, with a preference for the lower end of the range;

b. switches for permanently wired appliances are located between 400mm and 1200mm above the floor, unless needed at a higher level for particular appliances;

c. all switches and controls that require precise hand movements are located between 750mm and 1200mm above the floor;

d. simple push button controls that require limited dexterity are not more than 1200mm above the floor;

e. pull cords for emergency alarm systems are coloured red, located as close to a wall as possible and have two red 50mm diameter bangles, one set at 100mm and the other set between 800mm and 1000mm above the floor;

f. controls that need close vision are located between 1200mm and 1400mm above the floor so that readings may be taken by a person sitting or standing (with thermostats at the top of the range);

g. socket outlets are located consistently in relation to doorways and room corners, but in any case no nearer than 350mm from room corners;

h. light switches for use by the general public have large push pads and align horizontally with door handles within the range 900 to 1100mm, for ease of location when entering a room;

i. where switches described in 4.30(h) cannot be provided, lighting pull cords are set between 900mm and 1100mm above floor level, and fitted with a 50mm diameter bangle visually contrasting with its background and distinguishable visually from any emergency assistance pull cord;

j. the operation of switches, outlets and controls does not require the simultaneous use of both hands, except where this mode of operation is necessary for safety reasons;

k. switched socket outlets indicate whether they are 'on';

l. mains and circuit isolator switches clearly indicate that they are on or off;

m. front plates contrast visually with their backgrounds.

Aids to communication

Design considerations

4.31 People will benefit most if there is an integrated system for wayfinding, public address and hearing enhancement.

4.32 The appropriate choice of floor, wall and ceiling surface materials and finishes can help visually impaired people appreciate the boundaries of rooms or spaces, identify access routes and receive information. For example, glare and reflections from shiny surfaces, and large repeating patterns, should be avoided in spaces where visual acuity is critical as they will hamper communication for people with impaired vision, and those who lip read or use sign language. This would apply to locations such as reception areas with enquiry desks and speakers' rostrums in lecture halls.

4.33 The type and quality of public address, hearing enhancement and telephone systems should be chosen carefully to ensure intelligibility. The design of the acoustic environment should also ensure that audible information can be heard clearly.

4.34 Artificial lighting should be designed to give good colour rendering of all surfaces, without creating glare or pools of bright light and strong shadows. Where appropriate, lighting should illuminate the face of a person speaking, to make lip reading easier where one-to-one communication is necessary. Uplighters mounted at low or floor level can disorientate some visually impaired people and should be avoided.

4.35 In order to obtain the full benefit of attending public performances or taking part in discussions, a person with impaired hearing needs to receive a signal that is amplified in both volume and signal to noise ratio. The three systems commonly used to provide this enhanced level of sound are induction loop, infrared and radio. Sound field systems are also increasingly being used, particularly in educational establishments. In larger spaces, provision needs to be made for a permanent system, but in small meeting rooms, a portable induction loop would be acceptable. It should be recognised that there is the danger where adjacent spaces each have an induction loop system that the signals may overlap.

Note: Detailed guidance on surface finishes, visual, audible and tactile signs, as well as the characteristics and appropriate choice and use of hearing enhancement systems, is available in BS 8300.

Provisions

4.36 Aids to communication will satisfy Requirement M1 if:

a. a clearly audible public address system is supplemented by visual information;

b. provision for a hearing enhancement system is installed in rooms and spaces designed for meetings, lectures, classes, performances, spectator sport or films, and at service or reception counters when they are situated in noisy areas or they are behind glazed screens;

c. the presence of an induction loop or infrared hearing enhancement system is indicated by the standard symbol;

d. telephones suitable for hearing aid users are clearly indicated by the standard ear and 'T' symbol and incorporate an inductive coupler and volume control;

e. text telephones for deaf and hard of hearing people are clearly indicated by the standard symbol;

f. artificial lighting is designed to be compatible with other electronic and radio frequency installations.

Section 5: Sanitary accommodation in buildings other than dwellings

OBJECTIVES

5.1   In principle, suitable sanitary accommodation should be available to everybody, including sanitary accommodation designed for wheelchair users, ambulant disabled people, people of either sex with babies and small children or people encumbered by luggage.

5.2   In multi-storey buildings, the consistent location of toilets on each floor can help people with learning difficulties to locate these facilities easily.

Sanitary accommodation generally

Design considerations

5.3   A number of issues need to be considered in connection with all forms of sanitary accommodation. These relate to the needs of people with visual or hearing impairments, people with learning difficulties and people whose lack of tactile sensitivity can cause them to be injured by touching hot surfaces. Taps and WC cubicle doors should be operable by people with limited strength or manual dexterity and doors to cubicles should be capable of being opened if a person has collapsed against them while inside the cubicle. Preferably, all doors to WC cubicles and wheelchair-accessible unisex toilets open out or, if they open in, the door swing should not encroach into the wheelchair turning space or minimum activity space. Where possible, light switches with large push pads should be used in preference to pull cords (see 4.28).

Provisions

5.4   Sanitary accommodation will satisfy Requirement M1 or M3 if:

a. any bath or washbasin tap is either controlled automatically, or is capable of being operated using a closed fist, e.g. by lever action;

b. terminal fittings comply with Guidance Note G18.5 of the Guidance Document relating to Schedule 2: Requirements for Water Fittings, of the Water Supply (Water Fittings) Regulations 1999, SI 1999/1148;

c. door handles and other ironmongery comply with provisions 3.10 (d) and (e) of 'Internal doors';

d. WC compartment doors, and doors to wheelchair-accessible unisex toilets, changing rooms or shower rooms are fitted with light action privacy bolts so that they can be operated by people with limited dexterity and, if required to self-close, can be opened using a force at the leading edge of not more than 30N from 0° (the door in the closed position) to 30° open, and not more than 22.5N from 30° to 60° of the opening cycle;

e. WC compartment doors, and doors to wheelchair-accessible unisex toilets, changing rooms or shower rooms have an emergency release mechanism so that they are capable of being opened outwards, from the outside, in case of emergency;

f. doors, when open, do not obstruct emergency escape routes;

g. any fire alarm emits a visual and audible signal to warn occupants with hearing or visual impairments;

h. any emergency assistance alarm system has:

   i. visual and audible indicators to confirm that an emergency call has been received;

   ii. a reset control reachable from a wheelchair and the WC, or from the wheelchair and the shower/changing seat;

   iii. a signal that is distinguishable visually and audibly from the fire alarm.

I. any lighting controls comply with the provisions for 'Switches and controls', see 4.30;

j. any heat emitters are either screened or have their exposed surfaces kept at a temperature below 43°C;

k. the surface finish of sanitary fittings and grab bars contrasts visually with background wall and floor finishes, and there is also visual contrast between wall and floor finishes.

Provision of toilet accommodation

Design considerations

5.5 Toilet accommodation needs to be suitable, not only for disabled people, but for all people who use the building. For disabled people, suitable toilet accommodation may take the form of a specially designed cubicle in separate-sex toilet washrooms, or a self-contained unisex toilet. For wheelchair users in particular, a self-contained unisex toilet is always the preferred option since, if necessary, a partner or carer of a different sex can enter to give assistance. Wheelchair-accessible unisex toilets should always be provided in addition to any wheelchair-accessible accommodation in separate-sex toilet washrooms. Wheelchair-accessible unisex toilets should not be used for baby changing.

5.6 The provision of an enlarged cubicle in a separate-sex toilet washroom can be of benefit to ambulant disabled people, as well as parents with children and people (e.g. those with luggage) who need an enlarged space. In large building developments, separate facilities for baby changing and an enlarged unisex toilet incorporating an adult changing table are desirable. Facilities incorporating adult changing tables are more commonly known as Changing Places Toilets and further guidance is available from the Changing Places Campaign website (www.changing-places.org) or by reference to guidance in section 12.7 and Annex G of BS 8300.

Note: For specific guidance on the provision of sanitary accommodation in sports buildings, refer to 'Access for Disabled People'.

Provisions

5.7 The provision of toilet accommodation will satisfy Requirement M1 or M3 if:

a. where there is space for only one toilet in a building, it is of a wheelchair-accessible unisex type, but of greater width to accommodate a standing height wash basin;

b. at least one wheelchair-accessible unisex toilet is provided at each location in a building where sanitary facilities are provided for use by customers and visitors to a building, or by people working in the building;

c. at least one WC cubicle is provided in separate-sex toilet accommodation for use by ambulant disabled people;

d. where there are four or more WC cubicles in separate-sex toilet accommodation, one of these is an enlarged cubicle for use by people who need extra space, in addition to any provision under 5.7(c).

Wheelchair-accessible unisex toilets

Design considerations

5.8 Wheelchair users should be able to approach, transfer to and use the sanitary facilities provided within a building. This requires the provision of a wheelchair-accessible unisex toilet. The relationship of the WC to the finger rinse basin and other accessories should allow a person to wash and dry hands while seated on the WC. The space provided for manoeuvring should enable wheelchair users to adopt various transfer techniques that allow independent or assisted use. It is important that the transfer space alongside the WC is kept clear to the back wall. When transferring to and from their wheelchair, some people need horizontal support rails. The rail on the open side is a drop-down rail, but on the wall side, it can be a wall-mounted grab rail (which is thought to give a more rigid handhold) set at a greater distance than normal from the wall or, alternatively, a second drop-down rail in addition to the wall-mounted grab rail where the grab rail is spaced at the minimum distance from the wall and therefore does not give the same degree of support.

5.9 A unisex toilet is approached separately from other sanitary accommodation. It is more easily identified than a wheelchair-accessible cubicle in a separate-sex toilet washroom and, provided it is used only by disabled people, it is more likely to be available when required. This is particularly important as some disabled people need to use a toilet more frequently than other users. The time needed to reach a wheelchair-accessible toilet should therefore be kept to a minimum when considering the location of unisex toilet accommodation. In addition, a unisex toilet enables one or two assistants of either sex to assist a disabled person. Consideration should be given to installing a chemical sanitary waste disposal unit in wheelchair-accessible WC accommodation. Some wheelchair users find it difficult to use a standard height WC seat and, for them, it is important that the WC pan can accept a variable height toilet seat riser. WC pans manufactured to the key dimensions given in BS EN 997:2012 WC pans and WC suites with integral trap would be acceptable.

Note: More detailed guidance on the various techniques used to transfer from a wheelchair to a WC, as well as appropriate sanitary and other fittings, is given in BS 8300.

Provisions

5.10 Wheelchair-accessible unisex toilets will satisfy Requirement M1 or M3 if:

a. one is located as close as possible to the entrance and/or waiting area of the building;

b. they are not located in a way that compromises the privacy of users;

c. they are located in a similar position on each floor of a multi-storey building, and allow for right- and left-hand transfer on alternate floors;

d. when more than one unisex toilet is available in other than multi-storey buildings, a choice of layouts suitable for left-hand and right-hand transfer is provided;

e. when it is the only toilet facility in the building, the width is increased from 1.5m to 2m and it includes a standing height washbasin, in addition to the finger rinse basin associated with the WC;

f. they are located on accessible routes that are direct and obstruction free;

g. doors are preferably outward opening and are fitted with a horizontal closing bar fixed to the inside face;

h. any wheelchair user does not have to travel:

   i. more than 40m on the same floor, unless a greater distance can be agreed with the building control body on the grounds that the circulation route is unobstructed, e.g. by the installation of doors with hold-open devices;

   ii. more than a 40m combined horizontal distance where the unisex toilet accommodation is on another floor of the building, but is accessible by passenger lift (if a lifting platform is installed, vertical travel to a unisex toilet is limited to one storey);

i. the minimum overall dimensions of, and the arrangement of fittings within, a wheelchair-accessible unisex toilet comply with Diagram 18;

j. where the horizontal support rail on the wall adjacent to the WC is set with the minimum spacing from the wall, an additional drop-down rail is provided on the wall side at a distance of 320mm from the centre line of the WC;

k. where the horizontal support rail on the wall adjacent to the WC is set so that its centre line is 400mm from the centre line of the WC, there is no additional drop-down rail;

l. the heights and arrangement of fittings in a wheelchair-accessible unisex toilet comply with Diagram 19 and, as appropriate, Diagram 20;

Diagram 18 Unisex wheelchair-accessible toilet with corner WC

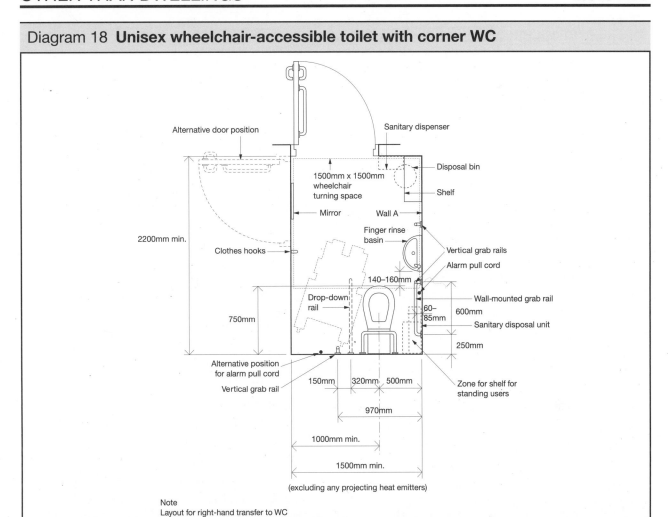

Alternative door position

Sanitary dispenser

Disposal bin

1500mm x 1500mm wheelchair turning space

Shelf

Mirror

Wall A

Finger rinse basin

Vertical grab rails

Alarm pull cord

2200mm min.

Clothes hooks

140–160mm

Drop-down rail

Wall-mounted grab rail

60–85mm

600mm

Sanitary disposal unit

750mm

250mm

Alternative position for alarm pull cord

Vertical grab rail

150mm 320mm 500mm

Zone for shelf for standing users

970mm

1000mm min.

1500mm min.

(excluding any projecting heat emitters)

Note
Layout for right-hand transfer to WC

Diagram 19 Heights and arrangement of fittings in a unisex wheelchair-accessible toilet (looking towards wall A in diagram 18)

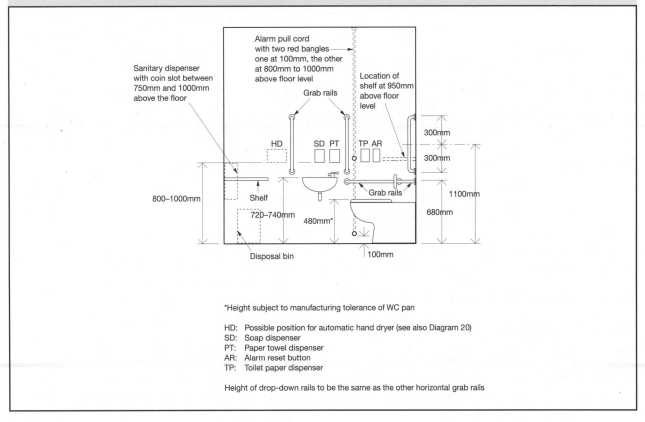

Sanitary dispenser with coin slot between 750mm and 1000mm above the floor

Alarm pull cord with two red bangles one at 100mm, the other at 800mm to 1000mm above floor level

Location of shelf at 950mm above floor level

Grab rails

300mm

HD   SD PT   TP AR

300mm

800–1000mm

Shelf

Grab rails

1100mm

720–740mm

480mm*

680mm

Disposal bin

100mm

*Height subject to manufacturing tolerance of WC pan

HD: Possible position for automatic hand dryer (see also Diagram 20)
SD: Soap dispenser
PT: Paper towel dispenser
AR: Alarm reset button
TP: Toilet paper dispenser

Height of drop-down rails to be the same as the other horizontal grab rails

Diagram 20 **Height of various fittings in toilet accommodation**

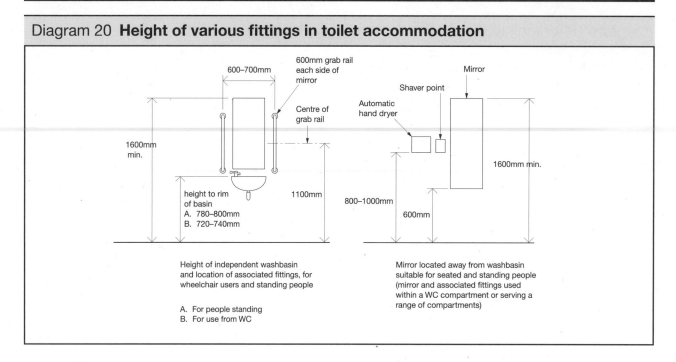

600–700mm

600mm grab rail each side of mirror

Mirror

Shaver point

Automatic hand dryer

Centre of grab rail

1600mm min.

height to rim of basin
A. 780–800mm
B. 720–740mm

1100mm

800–1000mm

600mm

1600mm min.

Height of independent washbasin and location of associated fittings, for wheelchair users and standing people

A. For people standing
B. For use from WC

Mirror located away from washbasin suitable for seated and standing people (mirror and associated fittings used within a WC compartment or serving a range of compartments)

m. an emergency assistance alarm system is provided, complying with 5.4;

n. the emergency assistance call signal outside the toilet compartment is located so that it can be easily seen and heard by those able to give assistance;

o. an emergency assistance pull cord is easily identifiable (see 4.30(e)) and reachable from the WC and from the floor close to the WC;

p. any heat emitters are located so that they do not restrict the minimum clear wheelchair manoeuvring space, nor the space beside the WC used for transfer from the wheelchair to the WC;

q. WC pans conform to BS EN 997:2012 in terms of key dimensions in order to accommodate the use of a variable height toilet seat riser (see 5.9);

r. cisterns for WCs that will be used by wheelchair users have their flushing mechanism positioned on the open or transfer side of the space, irrespective of handing.

Toilets in separate-sex washrooms

Design considerations

5.11 Ambulant disabled people should have the opportunity to use a WC compartment within any separate-sex toilet washroom. The compartment should be fitted with support rails, and include a minimum activity space to accommodate people who use crutches, or otherwise have impaired leg movements. The presence of this facility helps avoid unnecessary travel to unisex toilet accommodation. Some ambulant disabled people find it difficult to use a standard height WC seat and, for them, it is important that the WC pan can accept a variable height toilet seat riser.

5.12 Separate-sex toilet washrooms above a certain size should also include an enlarged WC cubicle for use by people who need extra space, e.g. parents with children and babies, people carrying luggage and also ambulant disabled people. Consideration should be given to installing a fold-down table, e.g. for baby changing. Standard WC compartments should also have a minimum manoeuvring space clear of any door swing.

5.13 Where a separate-sex toilet washroom can be accessed by wheelchair users, it should be possible for them to use both a urinal, where appropriate, and a washbasin at a lower height than is provided for other users. The relative numbers of urinals for men and WC compartments for women has been the subject of recent research. In general, the findings indicate that there should be at least the same number of

WCs (for women) as urinals (for men) and for some building types, e.g. large retail buildings, at least twice as many. Consideration should be given to providing a low level urinal for children in male washrooms.

Note: More detailed guidance on appropriate sanitary and other fittings is given in BS 8300.

Provisions

5.14 WC compartments within separate-sex toilet washrooms will satisfy Requirement M1 or M3 if:

a. the swing of any inward opening doors to standard WC compartments is such that a 450mm diameter manoeuvring space is maintained between the swing of the door, the WC pan and the side wall of the compartment;

b. the minimum dimensions of compartments for ambulant disabled people, including the activity space, and the arrangement of grab bars and other fittings within the compartment, comply with Diagram 21;

c. doors to compartments for ambulant disabled people are preferably outward opening and are fitted with a horizontal closing bar fixed to the inside face;

d. an enlarged compartment for those who need extra space (based on the compartment for ambulant disabled people) is 1200mm wide and includes a horizontal grab bar adjacent to the WC, a vertical grab bar on the rear wall and space for a shelf and fold-down changing table;

e. any compartment for use by ambulant disabled people has a WC pan that conforms to BS EN 997:2012 in terms of key dimensions, in order to accommodate the use of a variable height toilet seat riser (see 5.9 and 5.11);

f. a wheelchair-accessible compartment (where provided) has the same layout and fittings as the unisex toilet;

g. any wheelchair-accessible washroom has at least one washbasin with its rim set at 720 to 740mm above the floor and, for men, at least one urinal with its rim set at 380mm above the floor, with two 600mm long vertical grab bars with their centre lines at 1100mm above the floor, positioned either side of the urinal.

Wheelchair-accessible changing and shower facilities

Design considerations

5.15 A choice of shower layout combined with the correct location of shower controls and fittings will allow disabled people to use the facilities independently or be assisted by others when necessary. For guidance on the provision of en-suite shower facilities associated with hotel bedrooms, see 4.19.

5.16 In buildings where changing facilities are associated with showering facilities, many disabled people will be content to use changing and shower areas that are open but provided with subdivisions, whereas some will require the privacy and convenience of an individual self-contained cubicle or compartment. The dimensions

---

Diagram 21 **WC cubicle for ambulant disabled people**

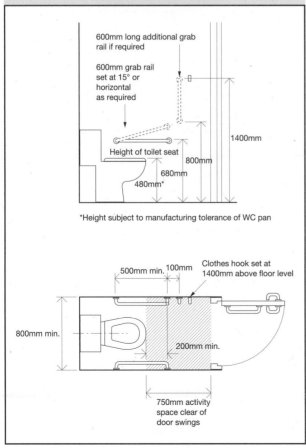

600mm long additional grab rail if required

600mm grab rail set at 15° or horizontal as required

Height of toilet seat

1400mm

800mm

680mm

480mm*

*Height subject to manufacturing tolerance of WC pan

Clothes hook set at 1400mm above floor level

500mm min. 100mm

800mm min.

200mm min.

750mm activity space clear of door swings

---

of the self-contained compartment allow space for a helper. Any combined facility should be divided into distinct 'wet' and 'dry' areas. In open changing and shower areas, it may be difficult to provide a configuration of handrails, controls and seat suitable for all disabled people to use. Individual self-contained accommodation is therefore preferred although, if it contains a WC, it should not be the only wheelchair-accessible toilet accommodation.

5.17 In the case of individual changing rooms not associated with showering, e.g. in clothes shops, the dimensions and fittings recommended for an individual self-contained changing cubicle in a sports building should be provided. In large building complexes, such as retail parks and large sports centres, there should be one wheelchair-accessible unisex toilet capable of including an adult changing table.

Note 1: For sports buildings, details of different types of changing and shower facilities are given in 'Access for Disabled People'.

Note 2: More detailed guidance on appropriate sanitary and other fittings is given in BS 8300.

Provisions

5.18 Wheelchair-accessible changing and shower facilities will satisfy Requirement M1 or M3 if:

For changing and shower facilities

a. a choice of layouts suitable for left-hand and right-hand transfer is provided when more than one individual changing compartment or shower compartment is available;

b. they are provided with wall-mounted drop-down support rails and wall-mounted slip-resistant tip-up seats (not spring loaded);

c. in communal shower facilities and changing facilities, they are provided with subdivisions that have the same configuration of space and equipment as for self-contained facilities but without doors;

d. in sports facilities, individual self-contained shower facilities and changing facilities are available in addition to communal separate-sex facilities;

e. an emergency assistance pull cord, complying with 4.30(e), is easily identifiable and reachable from the wall-mounted tip-up seat, or from the floor;

f. an emergency assistance alarm system complying with 5.4(h) is provided;

g. facilities for limb storage are included for the benefit of amputees;

For changing facilities

h. the minimum overall dimensions of, and the arrangement of equipment and controls within, individual self-contained changing facilities comply with Diagram 22;

i. when associated with shower facilities, the floor of a changing area is level and slip resistant when dry or when wet;

j. there is a manoeuvring space 1500mm deep in front of lockers in self-contained or communal changing areas;

For shower facilities

k. individual self-contained shower facilities comply with Diagram 23;

l. where showers are provided in commercial developments for the benefit of staff, at least one wheelchair-accessible shower compartment complying with Diagram 23 should be provided;

m. a shower curtain, which encloses the seat and the rails when they are in a horizontal position, can be operated from the shower seat;

n. a shelf that can be reached from the shower seat or from the wheelchair, before or after transfer, is provided for toiletries;

o. the floor of the shower and shower area is slip resistant and self-draining;

p. a shower terminal fitting complies with Guidance Note G18.5 of the Guidance Document relating to Schedule 2:

Diagram 22 An example of a self-contained changing room for individual use

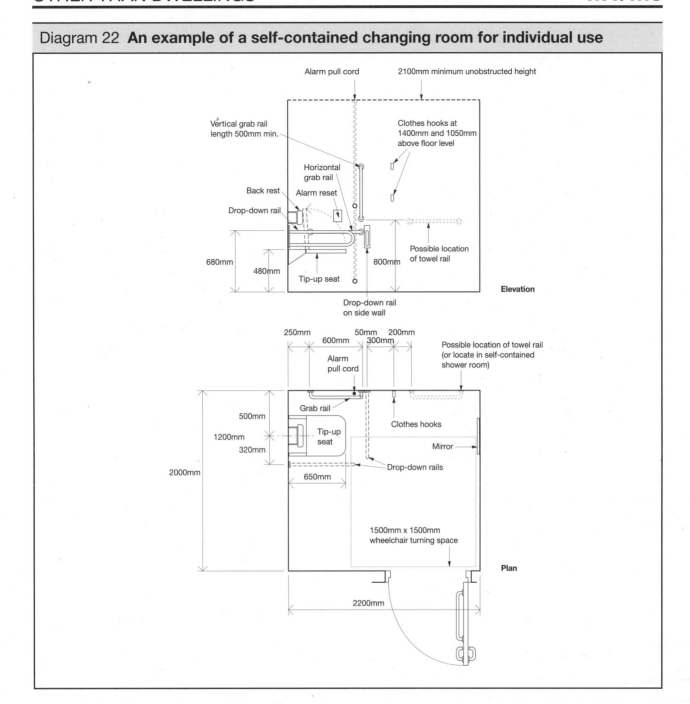

Requirement for Water Fittings, of the Water Supply (Water Fittings) Regulations 1999, SI 1999/1148, and the markings on the shower control are logical and clear;

q. where wheelchair-accessible shower facilities are available in communal areas, shower controls are positioned between 750 and 1000mm above the floor;

For shower facilities incorporating a WC

r. the minimum overall dimensions of, and the arrangement of fittings within, an individual self-contained shower area incorporating a corner WC, e.g. in a sports building, comply with Diagram 24;

s. a choice of left-hand and right-hand transfer layouts is available when more than one shower area incorporating a corner WC is provided.

Note: Guidance prepared by the Health and Safety Executive on the slip resistance of floor surfaces is given in Annex C of BS 8300.

Diagram 23 **An example of a self-contained shower room for individual use**

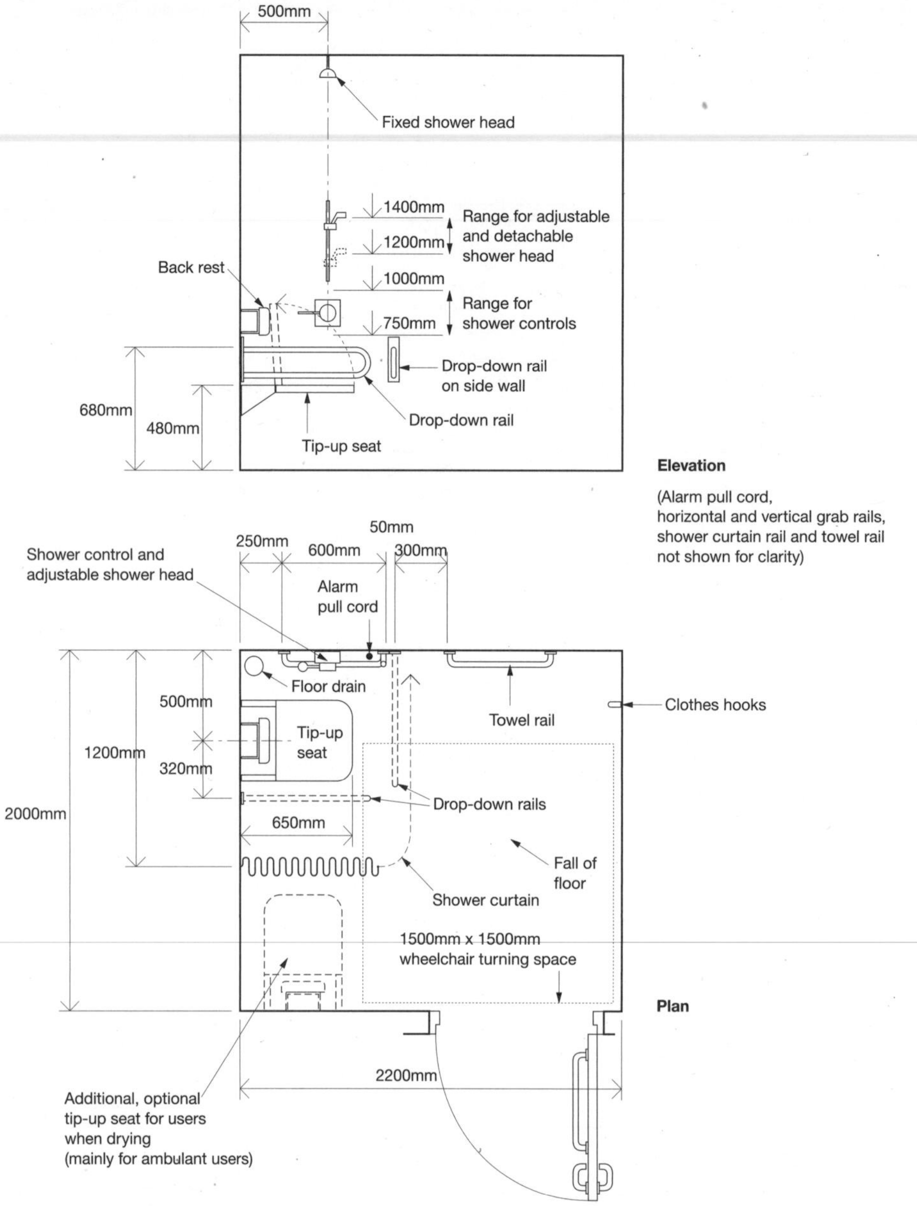

500mm

Fixed shower head

1400mm
1200mm Range for adjustable and detachable shower head

1000mm
750mm Range for shower controls

Back rest

Drop-down rail on side wall

Drop-down rail

680mm
480mm

Tip-up seat

Elevation

(Alarm pull cord, horizontal and vertical grab rails, shower curtain rail and towel rail not shown for clarity)

Shower control and adjustable shower head

250mm 600mm 50mm 300mm

Alarm pull cord

Floor drain

500mm
Tip-up seat

Towel rail

Clothes hooks

1200mm
320mm

Drop-down rails

2000mm
650mm

Fall of floor

Shower curtain

1500mm x 1500mm wheelchair turning space

Plan

Additional, optional tip-up seat for users when drying (mainly for ambulant users)

2200mm

Diagram 24 An example of a shower room incorporating a corner WC for individual use

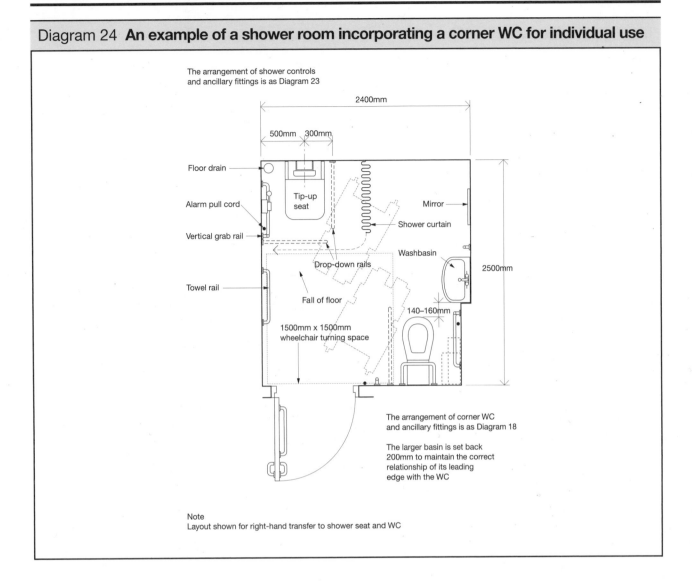

The arrangement of shower controls and ancillary fittings is as Diagram 23

2400mm

500mm 300mm

Floor drain

Tip-up seat

Alarm pull cord

Mirror

Shower curtain

Vertical grab rail

Washbasin

2500mm

Drop-down rails

Towel rail

Fall of floor

140–160mm

1500mm x 1500mm wheelchair turning space

The arrangement of corner WC and ancillary fittings is as Diagram 18

The larger basin is set back 200mm to maintain the correct relationship of its leading edge with the WC

Note
Layout shown for right-hand transfer to shower seat and WC

Wheelchair-accessible bathrooms

Design considerations

5.19 Wheelchair users and ambulant disabled people should be able to wash or bathe either independently or with assistance from others. The relationship of the bath to other sanitary fittings, and to the space required for manoeuvring, is therefore critical. Providing a choice of bathroom layout, wherever possible, will meet the needs of many disabled people and help maintain their independence.

5.20 The guidance covered here applies to wheelchair-accessible bathing facilities where provided in buildings such as hotels, motels, relatives' accommodation in hospitals, and to student accommodation and sports facilities where baths are provided as an alternative, or as a supplement, to showers. For guidance on the provision of en-suite

bathrooms associated with hotel bedrooms, see 4.19.

Note: More detailed guidance on appropriate sanitary and other fittings, including facilities for the use of mobile and fixed hoists is given in BS 8300.

Provisions

5.21 Wheelchair-accessible bathrooms will satisfy Requirement M1 or M3 if:

a. the minimum overall dimensions of, and the arrangement of fittings within, a bathroom for individual use incorporating a corner WC comply with Diagrams 25 and 26;

b. a choice of layouts suitable for left-hand and right-hand transfer is provided when more than one bathroom for individual use incorporating a corner WC is available;

Diagram 25 An example of a bathroom incorporating a corner WC

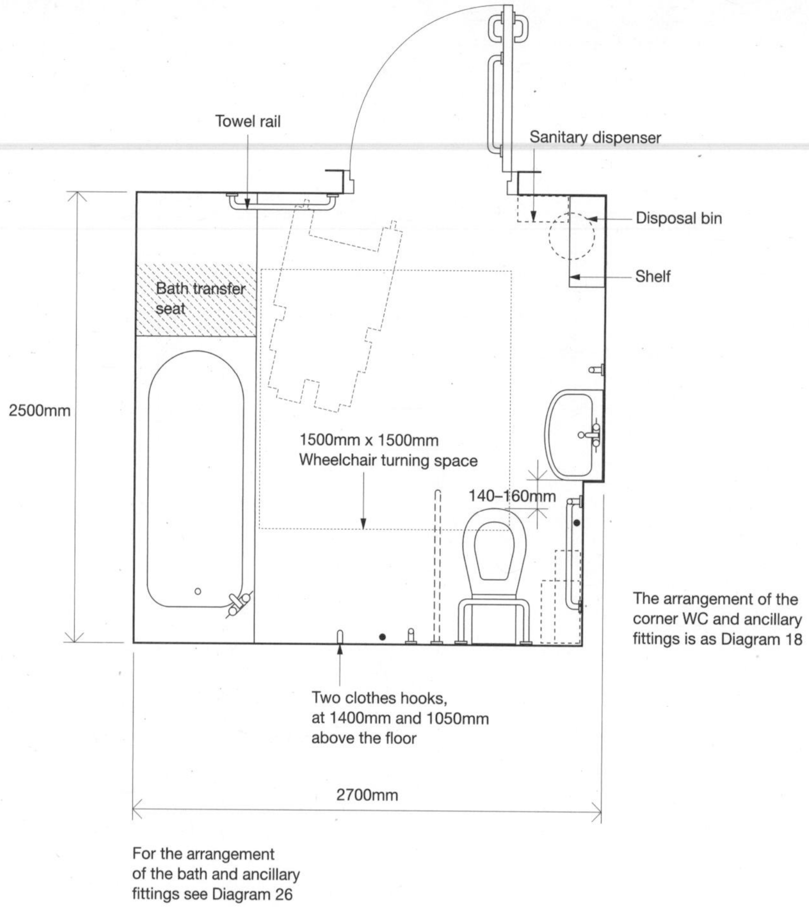

Towel rail

Sanitary dispenser

Disposal bin

Bath transfer seat

Shelf

2500mm

1500mm x 1500mm
Wheelchair turning space

140–160mm

The arrangement of the corner WC and ancillary fittings is as Diagram 18

Two clothes hooks,
at 1400mm and 1050mm
above the floor

2700mm

For the arrangement
of the bath and ancillary
fittings see Diagram 26

Note
Layout shown for right-hand transfer to bath and WC

c. the floor of a bathroom is slip resistant when dry or when wet;

d. the bath is provided with a transfer seat, 400mm deep and equal to the width of the bath;

e. doors are preferably outward opening and are fitted with a horizontal closing bar fixed to the inside face;

f. an emergency assistance pull-cord complying with 4.30(e) is easily identifiable and reachable from the bath or from the floor;

g. an emergency assistance alarm system complying with 5.4(h) is provided.

Note: Guidance prepared by the Health and Safety Executive on the slip resistance of floor surfaces is given in Annex C of BS 8300.

Diagram 26 Grab rails and fittings associated with a bath

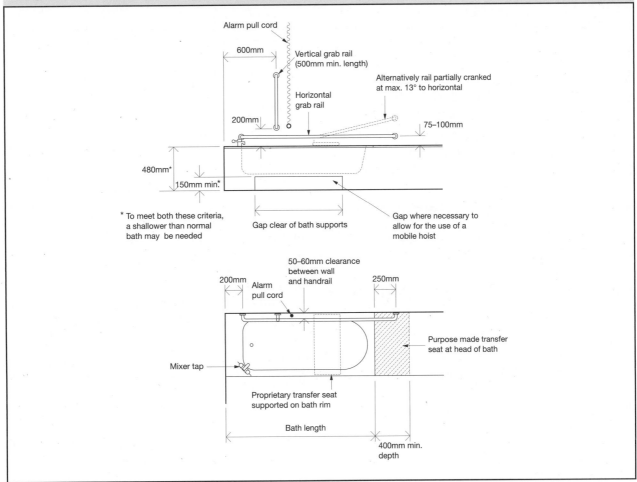

Alarm pull cord

600mm

Vertical grab rail (500mm min. length)

Alternatively rail partially cranked at max. 13° to horizontal

Horizontal grab rail

200mm

75–100mm

480mm*

150mm min.*

* To meet both these criteria, a shallower than normal bath may be needed

Gap clear of bath supports

Gap where necessary to allow for the use of a mobile hoist

50–60mm clearance between wall and handrail

200mm

Alarm pull cord

250mm

Mixer tap

Purpose made transfer seat at head of bath

Proprietary transfer seat supported on bath rim

Bath length

400mm min. depth

Section 6: Means of access to and into the dwelling

OBJECTIVE

6.1 The objective is to make reasonable provision within the boundary of the plot of the dwelling for a disabled person to approach and gain access into the dwelling from the point of alighting from a vehicle which may be within or outside the plot. In most circumstances it should be possible to provide a level or ramped approach.

6.2 On plots which are reasonably level, wheelchair users should normally be able to approach the principal entrance. Exceptionally, for more steeply sloping plots, it is considered reasonable to provide for stick or crutch users (see paragraph 6.9).

6.3 On plots where wheelchair users have approached the entrance, they should also be able to gain access into the dwelling-house and entrance level flats.

Approach to the dwelling

Design considerations

6.4 The provision of an approach which can be used by disabled people, including wheelchair users, will often be a matter of practicability. Variations in topography, available plot area or the distance of the dwelling from the point of access may all influence the type of approach that can be provided.

6.5 Normally, the provisions will apply to the approach to the principal entrance. However, if that is not possible in a particular situation, it would be reasonable to apply them to the approach to a suitable alternative entrance.

6.6 The approach should be as safe and as convenient for disabled people as is reasonable and, ideally, be level or ramped. However, on steeply sloping plots, a stepped approach would be reasonable.

6.7 If a stepped approach to the dwelling is unavoidable, the aim should be for the steps to be designed to suit the needs of ambulant disabled people (see paragraph 6.17).

6.8 Alternatively, the presence of a driveway might provide a better opportunity for creating a level or ramped approach, particularly if it also provides the sole means of approach for visitors who are disabled. The driveway itself could be designed as the approach from the pavement or footpath or may be the place where visitors park. In such cases, a level or ramped approach may be possible from the car parking space, particularly on steeply sloping plots.

6.9 It is important that the surface of an approach available to a wheelchair user should be firm enough to support the weight of the user and his or her wheelchair and smooth enough to permit easy manoeuvre. It should also take account of the needs of stick and crutch users. Loose laid materials, such as gravel and shingle, are unsuitable for the approach.

6.10 The width of the approach, excluding space for a parked vehicle, should take account of the needs of a wheelchair user, or a stick or crutch user (see paragraph 6.13).

Note: Account will also need to be taken of planning requirements, such as for new building within conservation areas. Location and arrangement of dwellings on the site is a matter for planning, whereas the internal layout and construction of the dwellings is a matter for building control.

Provisions

6.11 Requirement M1 will be satisfied, if, within the plot of the dwelling, a suitable approach is provided from the point of access to the entrance. The point of access should be reasonably level and the approach should not have cross-falls greater than 1:40.

6.12 The whole, or part, of the approach may be a driveway.

Level approach

6.13 A 'level' approach will satisfy Requirement M1 if its gradient is not steeper than 1:20, its surface is firm and even and its width is not less than 900mm.

Ramped approach

6.14 If the topography is such that the route from the point of access towards the entrance has a plot gradient exceeding 1:20 but not exceeding 1:15, Requirement M1 will be satisfied if a ramped approach is provided.

6.15 A ramped approach will satisfy Requirement M1 if it:

a. has a surface which is firm and even;

b. has flights whose unobstructed widths are at least 900mm;

c. has individual flights not longer than 10m for gradients not steeper than 1:15, or 5m for gradients not steeper than 1:12; and

d. has top and bottom landings and, if necessary, intermediate landings, each of whose lengths is not less than 1.2m, exclusive of the swing of any door or gate which opens onto it.

Stepped approach

6.16 If the topography is such that the route (see paragraphs 6.6–6.8) from the point of access to the entrance has a plot gradient exceeding 1:15, Requirement M1 will be satisfied if a stepped approach is provided.

6.17 A stepped approach will satisfy Requirement M1 if:

a. it has flights whose unobstructed widths are at least 900mm;

b. the rise of a flight between landings is not more than 1.8m;

c. it has top and bottom and, if necessary, intermediate landings, each of whose lengths is not less than 900mm;

d. it has steps with suitable tread nosing profiles (see Diagram 27) and the rise of each step is uniform and is between 75mm and 150mm;

Diagram 27 External step profiles

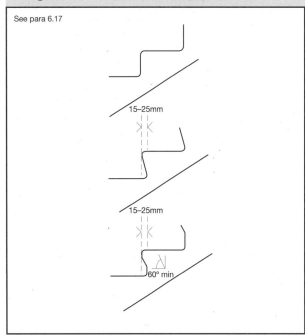

See para 6.17

15–25mm

15–25mm

60° min

e. the going of each step is not less than 280mm, which for tapered treads should be measured at a point 270mm from the 'inside' of the tread; and

f. where the flight comprises three or more risers, there is a suitable continuous handrail on one side of the flight. A suitable handrail should have a grippable profile; be between 850mm and 1000mm above the pitch line of the flight; and extend 300mm beyond the top and bottom nosings.

Approach using a driveway

6.18 Where a driveway provides a means of approach towards the entrance, it will satisfy Requirement M1 if the driveway provides an approach past any parked cars in accordance with paragraphs 6.11–6.17 above.

Access into the dwelling

Design considerations

6.19 Where the approach to the entrance consists of a level or ramped approach (see paragraphs 6.13–6.15), an accessible threshold at the entrance should be provided. An accessible threshold into entrance level flats should also be provided.

6.20 In exceptional circumstances where the approach to the entrance consists of a stepped approach (see paragraph 6.16), it would still be reasonable to provide an accessible threshold. If a step into the dwelling is unavoidable, the rise should be no more than 150mm.

Provisions

6.21 If the approach to the dwelling or block of flats consists of a level or ramped approach, Requirement M1 will be satisfied if an accessible threshold is provided into the entrance. The design of an accessible threshold should also satisfy the requirements of Part C2: 'Dangerous and offensive substances' and Part C4: 'Resistance to weather and ground moisture'.

Note: General guidance on design considerations for accessible thresholds has been published separately by The Stationery Office as 'Accessible thresholds in new housing: guidance for house builders and designers'.

Entrance doors

Design considerations

6.22 The provision of an appropriate door opening width will enable a wheelchair user to manoeuvre into the dwelling.

Provisions

6.23 Requirement M1 will be satisfied if an external door providing access for disabled people has a minimum clear opening width of 775mm.

Note: For dwellings, the clear opening width is taken from the face of the door stop on the latch side to the face of the door when open at 90° (i.e. no change from the 1999 edition of AD M).

Section 7: Circulation within the entrance storey of the dwelling

OBJECTIVE

7.1 The objective is to facilitate access within the entrance storey or the principal storey of the dwelling, into habitable rooms and a room containing a WC, which may be a bathroom on that level.

Corridors, passageways and internal doors within the entrance storey

Design considerations

7.2 Corridors and passageways in the entrance storey should be sufficiently wide to allow convenient circulation by a wheelchair user. Consideration should be given to the effects of local obstruction by radiators and other fixtures.

7.3 It will be necessary to consider the layout of a room served by an alternative to the principal entrance in order that a wheelchair user can pass through it to reach the remainder of the entrance storey.

7.4 Internal doors need to be of a suitable width to facilitate wheelchair manoeuvre. A wider door than generally provided would allow easier manoeuvring when it is necessary for a wheelchair user to turn into a door opening, as opposed to approaching it head-on.

Provisions

7.5 Requirement M1 will be satisfied if:

a. a corridor or other access route in the entrance storey or principal storey serving habitable rooms and a room containing a WC (which may be a bathroom) on that level has an unobstructed width in accordance with Table 4;

b. a short length (no more than 2m) of local permanent obstruction in a corridor, such as a radiator, would be acceptable provided that the unobstructed width of the corridor is not less than 750mm for that length, and the local permanent

obstruction is not placed opposite a door to a room if it would prevent a wheelchair user turning into or out of the room; and

c. doors to habitable rooms and a room containing a WC have minimum clear opening widths shown in Table 4, when accessed by corridors or passageways whose widths are in accordance with those listed in Table 4.

Table 4 shows the minimum widths of corridors and passageways that would be necessary to enable wheelchair users to turn into and out of a range of doorway widths.

Table 4	**Minimum widths of corridors and passageways for a range of doorway widths**
Doorway clear opening width (mm)	**Corridor/passageway width (mm)**
750 or wider	900 (when approach head-on)
750	1200 (when approach not head-on)
775	1050 (when approach not head-on)
800	900 (when approach not head-on)

Diagram 28 Corridors, passages and internal doors

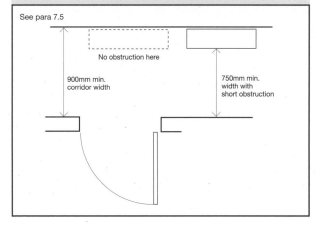

See para 7.5

No obstruction here

900mm min. corridor width

750mm min. width with short obstruction

Vertical circulation within the entrance storey

Design considerations

7.6 In exceptional circumstances, where severely sloping plots are involved, a stepped change of level within the entrance storey may be unavoidable. In those instances, the aim should be to provide a stair of reasonable width for ambulant disabled people to negotiate the steps with assistance and for handrails on both sides. Approved Document K of the Building Regulations contains guidance on the design of private stairs in dwellings.

Provisions

7.7 A stair providing vertical circulation within the entrance storey of the dwelling will satisfy Requirement M1 if they comply with Approved Document K, section 1.

Section 8: Accessible switches and socket outlets in the dwelling

OBJECTIVE

8.1   The aim is to assist those people whose reach is limited to use the dwelling more easily by locating wall-mounted switches and socket outlets at suitable heights.

Design considerations

8.2   Switches and socket outlets for lighting and other equipment should be located so that they are easily reachable.

Provisions

8.3   A way of satisfying Requirement M1 would be to provide switches and socket outlets for lighting and other equipment in habitable rooms at appropriate heights between 450mm and 1200mm from finished floor level (see Diagram 29).

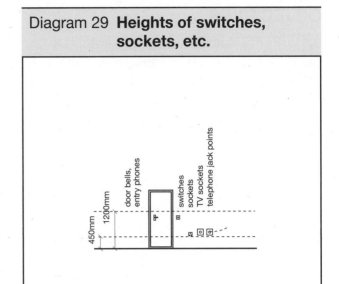

Diagram 29 **Heights of switches, sockets, etc.**

Section 9: Passenger lifts and common stairs in blocks of flats

OBJECTIVES

9.1 For buildings containing flats, the objective should be to make reasonable provision for disabled people to visit occupants who live on any storey.

9.2 The most suitable means of access for disabled people from one storey to another is a passenger lift. However, a lift may not always be provided.

Design considerations

9.3 If there is no passenger lift providing access between storeys, a general access stair should be designed to suit the needs of ambulant disabled people. In any event, a stair in a common area should be designed to be suitable for people with impaired sight.

9.4 Where a lift is provided, as a minimum a utility stair should be designed to be suitable for people with impaired sight. The lift should be suitable for an unaccompanied wheelchair user. Suitable provision should also be made for people with sensory impairments. Measures should also be adopted which give a disabled person sufficient time to enter the lift to reduce the risk of contact with closing doors.'

Provisions

Common stairs

9.5 Requirement M1 will be satisfied if a building containing flats, in which a passenger lift is not to be installed, is provided with a suitable stair in accordance with the relevant requirements in Approved Document K, section 1.

Note: Diagram 30 has been move to Approved Document K, Section 1, all other numbering remains the same

Lifts

9.6 Requirement M1 will be satisfied if a building, or a part of a building which contains flats above the entrance storey and in which passenger lift access is to be installed, is provided with a suitable passenger lift with a minimum load capacity of 400kg.

9.7 One way of satisfying Requirement M1 would be to provide a passenger lift which:

a. has a clear landing at least 1500mm wide and at least 1500mm long in front of its entrance;

b. has a door or doors which provide a clear opening width of at least 800mm;

c. has a car whose width is at least 900mm and whose length is at least 1250mm (other dimensions may satisfy Requirement M1 where shown by test evidence or experience in use, or otherwise, to be suitable for an unaccompanied wheelchair user);

d. has landing and car controls which are not less than 900mm and not more than 1200mm above the landing and the car floor, at a distance of at least 400mm from the front wall;

e. is accompanied by suitable tactile indication on the landing and adjacent to the lift call button to identify the storey in question;

f. has suitable tactile indication on or adjacent to lift buttons within the car to confirm the floor selected;

g. incorporates a signalling system which gives visual notification that the lift is answering a landing call and a 'dwell time' of five seconds before its doors begin to close after they are fully open: the system may be overridden by a door re-activating device which relies on appropriate electronic methods, but not a door edge pressure system, provided that the minimum time for a lift door to remain fully open is 3 seconds; and

h. when the lift serves more than three storeys, incorporates visual and audible indication of the floor reached.

Section 10: WC provision in the entrance storey of the dwelling

OBJECTIVES

10.1 The primary objective is to provide a WC in the entrance storey of the dwelling and to locate it so that there should be no need to negotiate a stair to reach it from the habitable rooms in that storey. Where the entrance storey contains no habitable rooms, it is reasonable to provide a WC in either the entrance storey or the principal storey.

Design considerations

10.2 The aim is to provide a WC within the entrance storey or the principal storey of a dwelling. Where there is a bathroom in that storey, the WC may be located in that bathroom. It will not always be practical for the wheelchair to be fully accommodated within the WC compartment.

Provision

10.3 Requirement M4 will be satisfied, if:

a. a WC is provided in the entrance storey of a dwelling which contains a habitable room; or where the dwelling is such that there are no habitable rooms in the entrance storey, if a WC is provided in either the entrance storey or the principal storey;

b. the door to the WC compartment opens outwards, and is positioned to enable wheelchair users to access the WC and has a clear opening width in accordance with Table 4 (door openings wider than the minimum in Table 4 allow easier manoeuvring and access to the WC by wheelchair users); and

c. the WC compartment provides a clear space for wheelchair users to access the WC (see Diagrams 31 and 32) and the washbasin is positioned so that it does not impede access.

Diagram 31 **Clear space for frontal access to WC**

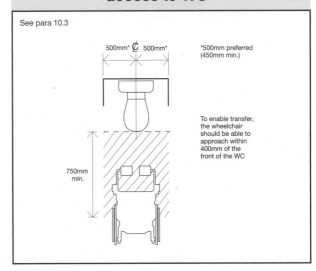

See para 10.3

Diagram 32 **Clear space for oblique access to WC**

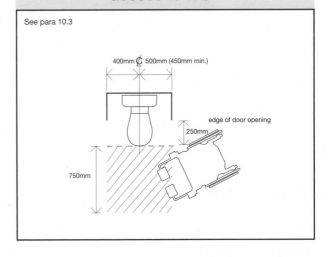

See para 10.3

Standards referred to

BS EN 81-70:2003
Safety rules for the construction and installation of lifts. Particular applications for passenger and good passengers lifts. Accessibility to lifts for persons including persons with disability. AMD 14675 2003, AMD 14751 2003.

BS 3402:1969
Specification for quality of vitreous china sanitary appliances. AMD 714 1971, AMD 4922 1989.

BS 5395-1:2000
Stairs, ladders and walkways. Code of practice for the design, construction and maintenance of straight stairs and winders.

BS 5588-8:1999
Fire precautions in the design, construction and use of buildings, Code of practice for means of escape for disabled people. AMD 14922 2004.

BS 7594:1993
Code of practice for audio-frequency induction-loop systems (AFILS).

BS 8300:2001
Design of buildings and their approaches to meet the needs of disabled people – Code of practice. AMD 15617 2005, AMD 15982 2005.

BS 8300: 2009 +A1:2010
(For Changing Places Toilets)
Design of buildings and their approaches to meet the needs of disabled people. Code of practice.

BS EN 997:2012
WC pans and WC suites with integral trap.

Other publications referred to

Department for Education and Employment (DfEE)

Building Bulletin 91 *Access for disabled people to school buildings. Management and design guide*, 1999. ISBN 0 11271 062 X

Building Bulletin 94 *Inclusive school design. Accommodating pupils with special educational needs and disabilities in mainstream schools*, 2001. ISBN 0 11271 109 X

Department for Environment, Food and Rural Affairs (DEFRA)

Water supply (water fittings) regulations 1999. Guidance document relating to Schedule 1: Fluid categories and Schedule 2: Requirements for water fittings. Available to download from www.defra.gov. uk/environment/water/industry/wsregs99/ guide/section8.htm

Department for Transport (DfT)

Inclusive mobility: A guide to best practice on access to pedestrian and transport infrastructure, 2002. Available to download from www.dft.gov.uk/stellent/groups/dft_mobility/documents/page/dft_mobility_503282-01.hcsp as hardcopy from DfT free literature service on 0870 1226236 (ref: IM/01) or as an audio cassette from the DfT Mobility and Inclusion Unit on 020 7944 6100 or Minicom 020 7944 3277

Department of National Heritage (DNH)

Guide to safety at sports grounds (The green guide). 4th edition, 1997. ISBN 0 11300 095 2

Department of the Environment Transport and the Regions (DETR)

Guidance on the use of tactile paving surfaces, 1998. Available to download from www.dft.gov.uk/stellent/groups/ dft_mobility/documents/pdf/dft_mobility_ pdf_503283.pdf

Disabled Persons Transport Advisory Committee (DPTAC)

Access directory – an online directory and search tool for references on accessibility guidance for the built environment. Available to download from www.dptac.gov.uk/

District Surveyors Association (DSA) and Association of British Theatre Technicians (ABTT)

Technical standards for places of entertainment, 2002. ISBN 1 90403 105 6

Football Stadia Improvement Fund (FSIF) and Football Licensing Authority (FLA)

Sports Ground and Stadia Guide No 1 Accessible stadia, 2003. ISBN 0 95462 930 2 Available to download from www.sportengland.org/disabled.pdf

JMU Access Partnership and Sign Design Society

Sign design guide, 2000.

Office of the Deputy Prime Minister (ODPM)

Planning and access for disabled people. A good practice guide, 2003.
ISBN 1 85112 604 X
Available to download from www.odpm.gov.uk/index.asp?id=1144644

Research Group for Inclusive Environments

Colour, contrast and perception. Design guidance for internal built environments, 2004.
Available from Research Group for Inclusive Environments, School of Construction Management, University of Reading,
tel 0118 9316734, textphone 0118 9864253

Sport England

Access for disabled people, 2002.
ISBN 1 86078 149 7
Available from the Sport England as hardcopy on 0870 5210255 or to download from www.sportengland.org/disabled.pdf

The Stationery Office (TSO)

Accessible thresholds in new housing. Guidance for house builders and designers, 1999. ISBN 0 11702 333 7

Legislation

Equality Act 2010
Equality Act 2010 (Disability) Regulations 2010
Lifting Operations and Lifting Equipment Regulations 1998, SI 1998/2307.

Lifts Regulations 1997, SI 1997/831.

Management of Health and Safety at Work Regulations 1999, SI 1999/3242.

Provision and Use of Work Equipment Regulations 1998, SI 1998/2306.

Water Supply (Water Fittings) Regulations 1999, SI 1999/1148.